WHERE THE OLD HIGHWAY HAD RUN

American Tales of the Road and Beyond

Chuck Klein
Illustrated by Jack Pumphrey

BeachHouse Books
Saint Charles Missouri USA

ISBN: 978-1-59630-098-9

Library of Congress LCCN 2015940156

BeachHouse
Books

www.beachhousebooks.com

For

Brittney

BIOGRAPHICAL INFORMATION

Chuck Klein, Author

In addition to duties as a full-time certified police officer for Woodlawn and Terrace Park, Ohio, Klein also served with the Switzerland County, Indiana Sheriff's office, was police photography instructor for the Norwood, Ohio Police Academy and a staff instructor for Tactical Defense Institute (www.tdiohio.com) . Though not an attorney, he holds a Bachelor of Laws degree from Blackstone School of Law and is an active member of the International Association of Law Enforcement Firearms Instructors (IALEFI). Klein's byline has appeared in national magazines including, but not limited to: Law & Order, Street Rod Action, Old Car News, Classic Car, P.I. Magazine, Law Officer Magazine, Gun Week, Guns & Ammo, American Police Beat. Contact and additional information may be found on his web site: www.chuckklein.com

Jack Pumphrey, Artist/Illustrator

Jack, a U.S. Air Force veteran (Strategic Air Command), served in Spain as a Nuclear Weapons Specialist during the early Cold War years. After paying his dues in the sales world for Addressograph-Multigraph Corporation he found his niche by demonstrating the capabilities of the 1250's by running off copies of his ink sketches of boats at Fisherman's wharf and other scenery around San Francisco.

In 1989 he struck out on his own as an independent graphics artist: Harbor Graphics & Design located in Gig Harbor, WA. He sold the business in 1998 and moved to Las Cruces, NM where he started Jack Pumphrey Arts. Working nationally with customers, prospects and referrals as a fine art watercolorist he honed his talents by doing commissions of classic cars and fine yacht. Utilizing his background in the printing industry, he created a line of Cruz'n Cards, note cards & posters, calendars, and presentation folders. Examples of his work and contact information may be found on his web site: www.jack-pumphrey.artistwebsites.com

Also By Chuck Klein

THE BEST OF CHUCK KLEIN, How Guns, Hot Rods, Police Ethics and Sacred Rights Shape America

GUNS IN THE WORKPLACE, A Manual for Private Sector Employers and Employees

THE WAY IT WAS, Nostalgic Tales of Hot Rods and Romance

INSTINCT COMBAT SHOOTING, Defensive Handgunning for Police

CIRCA 1957

LINES OF DEFENSE, Police Ideology and the Constitution

KLEIN'S CCW HANDBOOK, The Requisite for Those Who Carry Concealed Weapons

KLEIN'S UNIFORM FIREARMS POLICY, A manual for Private Sector Detectives and Security Agents

THE POWER OF GOD

THE BADGE, Stories and Tales From Both Sides of the Law

KLEIN FAMILY HISTORY, 1771 - 2006

Foreword

In "Where the Old Highway Had Run," Chuck Klein explores the many ways the automobile, that most star-spangled of inventions, slaked the American male's quests for power and velocity during the latter half of the previous century.

He does this in a way that's part fancy and part personal history, part pop and part Twilight Zone. He writes about heroes and other young men who might have been heroes had they not fallen tragically short of what they'd hoped would be. He writes about guns and four-wheeled dream machines, about the ghosts of rock 'n' roll when it was still new, still raw 'n' real.

In his fiction, Chuck Klein draws from a rich background that includes stretches as a small town police officer, private investigator, firefighter, tactical firearms instructor, unabashed defender of all things American and, from an early age, collector of speeding tickets.

He writes deftly, eloquently and convincingly about what he knows, and what he knows encompasses a whole big bunch of subjects. When he writes about power shifting and tires peeling, you can feel the lurch and hear the squeal. His style might put his reader to mind of Cormac McCarthy – austere, dark, unexpected, foreboding and more than a smidge dangerous. The way he writes, at least when he's writing from the imagination side of his brain, you get the impression something awful is about to happen. Reading through this book, it would be only a slight exaggeration to say I found myself looking over my shoulder a few times.

His essays, at least this time around, reveal a lighter side than his fiction. Chuck Klein very clearly had a fabulous time growing up. One might guess that perhaps part of his motivation for becoming a cop and a fireman was so he could drive at gale-force velocities without fear of adding to his speeding ticket collection. The chapters in this part of his latest book celebrate a bygone part of the American male spirit, the part that's drawn to exploring the forward edge of whatever frontiers their respective eras present.

Those boys and their hot rods had a good deal in common with cowboys, astronauts, explorers, entrepreneurs and other iconic types known for their willingness to venture into unknown territories and otherwise push limits. They make us think maybe we can do that, too. They inspire the rest of us to take risks now and then in order that we might live (read: experience) our lives more fully. That's the lesson I take away from Chuck Klein's latest.

David Wecker
Long-time Cincinnati Post columnist
Founder, BrandFlick
March 2015

Preface

Unlike full length books where the writer may use innumerable verbiage to describe events, persons or feelings; short stories must contain the beginning, middle and end in a very limited fashion. In other words, read slowly – every word counts.

Seventy-three years of living and a need to record it has given me the opportunity to write about a variety of subjects. Sans a research staff, all of these true and fiction stories are based on my personal experiences and/or the knowledge gained from the writings of others.

My paid gigs included: Lawn Care, Semi-Truck Driver, Salesman, Packaging Designer, Purchasing Agent, both Line & Staff Manager for a manufacturing company, Police Officer, Private Investigator, Author, Columnist, Farmer and Firearms Instructor. Other life-experiences endeavors comprise volunteer positions as a State Certified Fire-Fighter, Police Academy Photography Instructor and Kiwanis Club Member.

I got in the habit of penning daily activities from my father who habitually made a day-list of things he wanted to accomplish and then recorded what actually occurred in a journal. My diaries date to 1965 and have proven invaluable in settling arguments with family and friends as to whether I attended certain functions such as weddings, funerals or parties. They have also been most helpful in substantiating issues in court cases and, of course, writing stories and articles. I don't claim to be an expert on anything except with what I personally experienced. Having spent the majority of my working career as a cop and private detective, I'm well aware that eye witnesses can be wrong. However, I am also mindful that written records, especially when made in a timely manner, are far more accurate than mental recollections.

As of late, my wife and I have enjoyed a morning coffee together while reading from this memoire-reminisces about events from when we entered each other's lives.

Chuck Klein, 2015

ii

Illustrations by Jack Pumphrey:

Illustrations by Mo Mansoor:

Contents

I Fiction Stories

WHERE THE OLD HIGHWAY HAD RUN

It was one of those perfect fall days of low humidity, warm sunshine and occasional sun-blocking clouds that tempered the temperature. The deciduous trees, over-hanging the narrow two-lane highway, their branches reaching out as if to shake hands, placated the 36 year old printing salesman, Trent Hodwin. Cresting a small rise on the east bound country road that ran along the river in rural southern Ohio, he saw the flashing lights about a quarter mile ahead. Instinctively he backed off his company car, a 1971 Chevrolet Impala. Trent was alone, save for the double barrel shotgun lying on the back seat.

The father of two was in route to join a prospective customer for an afternoon of upland game hunting at a private lodge deep in the wooded ravines of this sparsely populated area. Though Quail hunting was his passion, Trent was only thinking of how he was going to convince the man to switch to his company's specialty of pre-printed corrugated.

Up ahead, Sheriff's Deputy Josh Johnston had just exited his 1972 Plymouth scout car after stopping to investigate an older model Ford pickup truck. He had tried to call in his location and the truck's license number, but the hills and valleys along this stretch of river road blocked his radio signal. The vehicle might be broken down, the driver taking a nap, passed out drunk or possibly poaching game. Police work always has plenty of surprises and was one reason why he liked the job. Six foot-two, muscular, dark-haired and 26 years old he had been on the force for almost three years. In that short time he had delivered one baby and arrested a score of felons, drunks and other unhappy men and women. Most of the time, he patrolled the county roads waiting to be needed.

Josh's off duty time, what little there was of it in the daylight hours, was almost entirely spent with is bride of two years and their 15 month old daughter, Kari. They lived in a house trailer on his father's farm that was set back from the road almost half a mile, next to where the old highway had run. He had only known dream-girl pretty, Kaycee, his wife, for a year before they 'had to' get married. To Josh, they fit like a tire to a wheel or a revolver to a holster. Both talked about building a proper home on this back forty if things worked out.

Rising early this morning for the day shift, Josh made his way into the kitchen by the always on stovetop light; annoying rays that bounced off the fridge, windows and polished wood cabinets. He often dressed in the kitchen so as not to disturb Kaycee. Uniformed up, he stepped out into the morning glow, paused next to the squad car to watch a couple of wind-tossed oak leaves swirl, twirl and dance across the apron in front of the carport. He and Kaycee had swirled, twirled and danced in that very spot the day they moved in. All that changed a few days ago. He smiled, unlocked the car door, fired the police packaged Plymouth, listened to be sure there was no radio traffic, and keyed the mic., "Four-David-Fourteen, two-six." Ten miles away in the county seat, the dispatcher replied, "Two-six, Four-David-Fourteen." And so the shift began.

Kaycee had been sleeping late for the past week not because she was tired, but because she dreaded the morning sickness . . . and she knew Josh, being the cop he was, had to know. She couldn't help it. It was the alcohol. It was Jail's fault. It was everyone's fault but hers.

J.L., her sister's ex, was called Jail because that's what J.L. sounded like from the vocal cords of an Appalachian. It hadn't been a long affair, but she needed this energetic love making that was so much better than missionary Josh, even though it always left her feeling dirty and evil. The last thing J.L. told her was he'd work something out with Josh as he wanted her to go with him to California.

Before Josh could close the door, a second vehicle pulled up behind him – a very familiar late model Camaro, deep blue in color. The driver also exited his vehicle and was walking toward the Deputy as Trent drove by. It was like seeing one single, stand-alone frame of an old 8mm film – one frame of dozens run by in seconds. In that lone frame, Trent glimpsed the Deputy being moved backward and what appeared to be a handgun in the hand of the Camaro driver.

In the tree line between the highway and the Ohio River, 42 year-old Omar T. Lickings hid and watched from only 50 yards away. Omar T. had been stalking a nice sized doe that had scampered into the woods after being almost hit by his truck a few minutes before the Sheriff's cruiser pulled up.

Trent slammed on the brakes of his Impala not sure what he saw or should do. Coming to a stop about 40 yards past the trio of cars, he climbed out, eyes fixed on the Deputy now lying on the roadway and the Camaro driver standing over his body – a gun surely in hand. The guy said nothing . . . and then fired a shot in Trent's direction. Trent, blinked, shook his head as if in disbelief and reached for the Fox Sterlingworth lying on the back seat. Twisting, clawing and fumbling with the box of shells sitting next to the shotgun he glanced up to see the Camaro driver advancing toward him. Trent was no stranger to violence having served as a forward observer in 'Nam and then finishing out his commitment as an MP at Ft. Bragg. Backing out from the car, he broke the gun open and without taking his eyes from the intruder, jammed two 20 gauge shells into the chambers as the Impala's rear window exploded. The Camaro driver, recognizing the silhouette of a double barreled shotgun, turned and headed back toward the downed Deputy who had now drawn his service revolver.

The pick-up driver, a poacher by necessity, could easily shoot the Camaro driver with his open-sighted .30-30 Winchester. However, Omar T., akin to the foxes and weasels he poached, slunk deeper into the scrub brush, his left eye twitching as it constantly did when he was in on the kill. Omar T. always used his middle initial because his brother was Omar Sam. They, a family of nine, lived up a holler deep in the hills of Simca County – a sparingly peopled region that was mostly streams and hills and woods. Their collection of oak and poplar sided shacks was just off the clear-cut that was where the old highway had run - thirty miles east of Josh and Kaycee Johnston's place. The stubble-bearded witness, holding a rifle of death in his hands, was on the return leg of a trip to Manchester where he had sold his stock of deer hides, eagle feathers and other ill-gotten wildlife parts. Jobs being scarce, he had learned his trade from his pappy who had done a stretch at Leavenworth for makin' shine. Omar T. also knew there was most likely a warrant out for him for the savage beating he'd given a man for sassing him a few weeks before last Sunday when they'd all been drinkin' pretty heavy.

Knowing the shotgun shells, filled with #8 shot, were not man-stopping beyond 40 yards, Trent fired the right barrel into the back of the Camaro driver. The man twitched as if stung by bees as Trent ran toward him to get within lethal range for his final shot.

The three armed men on the highway, almost simultaneously, and all in the line of fire of each other, exchanged gunfire.

Soon after her husband left, as Kari began talking gibberish to herself, Kaycee struggled out of bed. Kari looked just like her mother - light auburn hair to match pale brown eyes and a mouth that was always smiling even if she wasn't. Passing the front door, Kaycee paused to watch some leaves blowing in the wind and out beyond where the old highway had run. Paused to sort out her options with Josh, none of which she wanted to exercise.

Deputy Johnston, bleeding profusely and knowing the shot he had taken to the gut might be fatal, vowed to himself to kill his killer before he died. With dutiful grit he rolled onto his side, extracted his Model 19 Smith & Wesson magnum and, best he could - his eyesight becoming bleary - took aim.

5

Now, within 20 yards and closing, Trent, still running, shouldered his gun and fired the second barrel. The tight pattern of tiny BBs from the full choke left barrel struck the Camaro driver in the neck and spine staggering and buckling him. At that same instant Deputy Josh fired. The round from the magnum went over the top of the toppling Camaro driver and struck the MP/solider turned printing salesman square in the forehead, killing him instantly. The Camaro driver's reflexive and final shot struck the Deputy in the chest.

During this entire deadly encounter, the only audible words came from the mouth of the Sheriff's Deputy just before he was shot - the first time. Only one person at the scene - and still alive - heard those shouted words: Omar T. "NO, NO, DON'T DO IT, JAIL."

Omar T., his eye still twitching, pulled his stained and torn John Deere cap down a little lower before glancing up and down the highway. Except for a gaggle of geese off in the distance the countryside was clear and calm. Sliding out from the concealing brush and quickly approaching the carnage, he chuckled to himself; he didn't get the deer, but he sure as hell could make some money from all those guns lying on the pavement.

Knights of the 20th Century Tontine

The young man, in his late teens, pulled into the driveway, eager to show his father and great grandfather his latest acquisition, a '32 Ford. Almost at the same time a delivery man arrived with a package. Taking the carefully wrapped box, with the word "FRAGILE" stamped in red on all sides, into the library of the ancient

Tudor style house, he approached a much older man seated in a leather wingback.

"Pop." Then a little louder, "Grandpa, come outside for a minute I want to show you my new car. It's got all the extras."

The old timer knew cars. He had studied, and in some cases rubbed shoulders with, the best of the early engineers, customizers and racers. Men with the immortalized names of Iskenderian, Duntov, Barris, Fangio, Vukovich....

After the ritualistic inspection of the male bonding medium the two men returned to the den where the younger remembered the package. "I almost forgot, Pop, this came for you a little while ago."

"What is it Sonny?" the old man asked, settling into his overstuffed chair.

"I don't know Pop. It's from some law office back east and it sounds like it has liquid in it. You getting your Geritol by mail now?" The great grandson joked.

Staring at the proffered package the old man pushed back further into the cushions of the chair as if trying to distance himself from it. His mouth dropped open... "oh my God", escaped in a barely audible, raspy whisper.

"Grandpa, what's wrong? Are you okay?" The young gentleman crossed the room to take this ancient man's hand and search his frightened stare. "What is it, Pop?"

As recollections of events, forever melded to the sentimental portions of his mind, were forced to the present, the great grandfather's eyes soon began refocusing to a new intensity. "Get a couple of glasses and some ice, Sonny - and call your Dad in here. I've got a story to tell you."

A man with graying hair and his teenage son watched the great grandfather, in his 96th year, carefully and ceremoniously unwrap the package. Inside, sealed and encased in a solid wood box with a glass front panel, was a bottle of whisky. Attached to the outside of this shrine was a small brass hammer and a pouch. From this pouch he pulled a sheet of paper containing a list of names - names that had lines drawn through each, save one.

It was a very long time ago that they had met for the last time - a sort of reunion and farewell to one of the members who had but a short time to live.

Pretensions and pressures were checked at the door that night. Whatever problems they faced outside seemed far away and not important. Maybe it was seeing a "best" friend for the first time in two or three decades or just that deep feeling that only comes from the knowledge that to this group each truly belonged. They all knew that this assembly was just this night only and never again would they all be together. Maybe it came with the understanding that these were their roots and the distinct sensation of having come home again. Perhaps it was the familiarity and companionship of old friends, whose dues were also paid in full. It was a most memorable occasion.

It wasn't a large gathering, but 21 men out of a possible 36 wasn't too bad for an informal reunion. Some had died, some couldn't be found, most were graying and pot bellied, but all had, at one time, belonged to the KNIGHTS OF THE TWENTIETH CENTURY. Born so many years ago in a back alley garage of a Midwestern American city, The KNIGHTS hot rod club was not unlike other clubs of guys of that era. Back when rock & roll was in its infancy and fast cars had to be built by hand, the members bonded together to learn, help each other and talk engines, cars and speed. It was exciting being the center of attention during this era of historic automotive and musical upheaval.

...Big Bopper and Ben E. King
and LOVE IS A MANY SPLENDORED THING

"Here, you do it Sonny," the old man said handing the brass hammer to his great grandson.

Uncapping the bottle, which had been freed by breaking the glass front and without lifting his eyes from the list, the old man in his articulate way, began to pour forth a tale as if he had been rehearsing it all his life.

"Moonie, that's what they called me because I was the first to have Moon wheel covers on my rod, a '34 roadster that I had stuffed a Caddy engine into. It had a dropped front axle, chopped windshield and sported three-duces on the engine. Though I never got it completely finished it ran one-oh-three point six in the quarter mile. Not that this was the fastest in the club, but still very respectable. I didn't drive the roadster on the street much because something was always breaking so I kept a stock '39 Ford as my everyday car. The '39 was battered and shabby and second gear was stripped but, it ran quite reliably - those old flatheads would just run forever. The only thing I hated about that old relic was the hot, scratchy mohair seats. I got my share of carpet burns on my elbow trying to put my arm around a girl.

"Ah...the girls. It seems that we built and raced the cars to impress the girls and then whenever one of the guys had made enough of an impression she'd up and marry him and that would be the end of his hot rodding. Brides and all the 'comes-with' things associated with marriage probably contributed more to the demise of hot rodders and their clubs than anything else.

"You boys should have seen my bride! She was just about the prettiest thing that ever rode shotgun in an open roadster. I met her at a club dance - a sock hop we called it. She wore dungarees with the cuffs rolled up, in giant folds, almost to her knees. Her oversized shirt must have been her daddy's white dress button-down which also had huge folds of the sleeves all the way up her arm. The shirt tails were tied in a knot at her tiny waist, the slightest view of smooth soft skin barely visible. She wore her hair in a flip and she just had that fresh scrubbed look about her. Quite the opposite of me with my axle greased ducktails and form-fitted pink shirt with string tie and pleated slacks of charcoal gray. We rocked and rolled to the likes of Fat's Domino, Dale Wright, Buddy Holly and Larry Williams and when she put her head under my chin to 'Sixteen Candles' I knew it was something special. It was. Last week it would have been our 72nd anniversary...if she were still alive."

"Grandpa," the impatient teenager interrupted, "What about the bottle?"

"I'm comin' to that, Sonny. Don't rush me. Like I was sayin', it was at this gathering when we all got together for that one last time to say goodbye to Freddie. Now, nothing lasts forever, and by age 50 Freddie had developed a terminal case of cancer. Knowing that he was a short timer he kept himself busy hunting us down and planning this assembly to unite us for one last time and to establish his gift as a tontine - the bottle from which we are drinking at this very moment. He said he won the fifth at a club dance and being a teetotaler, just put it away. Freddie was Jewish and for that solemn affair he gave us a little insight into these ancient teachings. It was such a somber and commemorative occasion that I still remember his final words to us. Here was this dying compatriot, frail and weak, who looked each one of us in the eye as he decreed: 'In our faith it is believed that on Rosh Hashana, the New Year, it is written; on Yom Kippur, The Day of Atonement, it is sealed:

How many shall pass on,

How many shall come to be,

Who shall live to see ripe age,

And who shall not,

Who shall live,

And who shall die;

and so it must be, that only the last surviving member of THE KNIGHTS, the KNIGHTS OF THE TWENTIETH CENTURY, may toast his fellow members with - and savor the nectar of this - this last man bottle.'"

With a sigh of finality his still steady hand, rough, dried and cracked like a cheap paint job that had crystallized, picked up the small doubles glass. Using both hands, and not unlike how one would make an offering, raised the glass to just slightly above his head whispering, "I'll see you soon fellahs, keep 'em tuned up."

Warmed by the energy of the aged whiskey the old man rose from the security of his wingback and shuffled to the leaded windows overlooking the springtime embraced driveway. Just for an instant he was sure he saw Freddie waving from his NINETEEN thirty-two Ford, the one with the hopped-up Chevy engine and the plaque that said Knights, dangling from the back bumper. But, a deliberate wipe of the hand across his tear filling eyes revealed it was only his great grandson's...brand new TWENTY thirty-two Ford.

Author's Note: Though the story is fiction, there was a KNIGHTS of the 20th CENTURY hot rod club (est. 1955), we did have a reunion and we do have a tontine.

RECORD RUN

4-6-4 Baldwin Locomotive

> *He drove a hot rod Ford*
> *That could lay a fat black patch.*
> *That punk was a fool*
> *Whose daring had no match.*

Bonnie Sue knew, deep down, that he wasn't a "bad kid," but some of her friends and especially her mom didn't see it that way. Tommy, she felt, was just frustrated, though she wasn't sure what it was that he was so antsy about. He didn't do well in school, but he was very smart. He had, after all, figured out, without any help, how to take his car motor all apart and put it back together again. Besides, he had said he loved her. True, it was only once and in a fit of passion. It was on a Friday night, last month, at the drive-in. It was one of those Francis the Talking Mule flicks. The movie was boring so they just made out. Tommy kept trying to touch her where she didn't think he should. They fought, she cried, and Tommy said, "I really love you, Bonnie Sue, I mean it."

Bonnie Sue was sure that if only they could both finish school, get married (and Tommy in a good job) she'd be able to change his fast driving ways and other things that might need adjustments. Right now all she wanted was for her man to be here.

Tommy, at 16 and a half, was one of the more dedicated and speed crazed hot rodders in his sophomore class. Though he had never applied to one of the hot rod clubs for membership he was always thinking about joining - if they would take him. That was the rub. He'd already had two tickets for speeding and he had a reputation for fast driving on city streets. Hot rod clubs frowned on "squirrels," as they called them. He had never shied away from a traffic light race even when Bonnie Sue pouted about his high speed drags. Trouble was, he couldn't figure her out. She was pretty enough but she was always talking about love and all that mushy stuff and she only sometimes seemed to enjoy the drag racing - legal or otherwise. On their first few dates she had been all excited about his races even going so far as to taunt one of her girlfriends because this friend's steady drove a stocker.

But he was really burned up that she had so little regard for the fact that he held the record for the Train Run and now must defend that honor. Johnny Medford, with his daddy's brand new '55 Olds 88, had bested Tommy's record by at least 50 yards. For Tommy to let this go unchallenged would be like wearing your sister's bloomers or something equally unthinkable.

The troubles with Bonnie Sue culminated last night as they sat sipping Cokes in the lot of the West Chester Pike Bun Boy. Removing his arm from her shoulders to light a Lucky, Tommy asked, while trying to make it sound like a casual mention, "You want to ride with me when I go for the Train Run record tomorrow night?"

"Oh, Tommy, you're not going to do that again are you?" Not waiting for an answer she continued while tossing her pony tailed head in a dignified affront, "Tommy, I swear you're going to kill yourself one of these days with all this crazy...."

13

"Come on Baby I just have ta do it, ya dig. I'm not gonna to be no chicken hearted punk. I'll be the coolest cat in town if I beat that harry-high-schooler in his daddy's stocker."

"Oh Tommy, it's so dangerous I just worry that you'll be killed and I won't have you. I think you're the coolest guy at North Anderson anyway. Winning The Run can't make you any better in my eyes. Please, just for me don't do it," Bonnie Sue pleaded, all pouty faced.

"Aw, don't cry honey. I know you dig me and all, but this is something I just have to do. Besides it should be a snap. The last time I ended up backing off before the tracks, I had so much reserve power. And since then I've added dual points. And, hey, I'll put in new plugs in the morning to be extra safe! Don't worry," Tommy boasted, flicking his butt out the window of his faded black-topped '51 Ford with custom wheel covers

The object of his non-romantic desires, the '51, sported two-deuces with chrome racing air cleaners and glass-packed dual exhaust. It was not only fast but it sounded cool. In addition to the Mallory distributor he had recently added, he was planning to install Offenhauser high compression heads and maybe a Clay-Smith cam. His after school job at Wylie's Pure Oil Station didn't allow for many luxuries even though he was the highest paid of all the part-timers at $1.10 per hour.

1951 Ford

The rest of the evening was like, no-wheres-ville. They ended up, as they always did after a date, parked at the old abandoned army base down near the feed mill. Every time he tried to put the move on Bonnie Sue she'd scrunch up closer to her door and whimper about how she just wasn't in the mood. Chicks! Who could understand them? What kind of mood could she be in parked in a lover's lane? He took her straight home, not even walking her to the door. Then he pealed out because he knew it would make her angry.

Saturday, Train Run day, was chilly for September in Texas. Tommy had managed to install the new plugs between pumping gas and oil changes at Wylie's service station. The powerful flathead was running cherry and sounding very sweet. The soon-to-be nosed and decked rod had even gotten a wax job, compliments of the kids who hung out at the station. Kids, of course, meant anyone who wasn't old enough to have a driver's license. These youngsters, in hopes of being able to get a ride to the race area, would do almost anything for the privilege of seeing one of their idols in a run against death.

Just before quitting time, Johnny, riding in Delbert's straight eight Pontiac because his dad had stripped him of his driving rights upon finding out about the Train Run, stopped in at Wylie's.

"Hey Mr. Cool, I hear tell that you're gonna try to beat my record tonight?" Johnny sneered.

"Yeah, that's right sonny and I'll do it in a rod I built myself, not in my daddy's stocker," Tommy shot right back in a menacing tone.

"Why, I ought to climb out of here and...."

"Okay, Okay, punks. Enough of this tough-guy talk. Do you guys wanna belly-ache or race," Delbert demanded, taking control of the pre-race details. "Now listen up: me and Harry as witnesses, plus about a dozen kids, watched Johnny here, beat the train from the no passing sign through the intersection. Now if you want to beat this record you must start at the end of the guard rail. Ya dig, Tommy?"

"Well, I was thinking about starting halfway between the sign and the rail and...."

"No, no that won't do. You have to use a permanent fixture, dig. Otherwise cats would be claiming to have started at all kinds of locations and the record would be muddied. We talked about it and

15

that's the way it has to be. So, unless you're yellow we'll see ya five minutes before the eight-three-eight," Delbert stated.

Curling his lip, Tommy spat, "I ain't yella - I'll be there."

He didn't have time to be nervous only time to shower, change clothes and chow down with his mom and sister before heading for Bonnie Sue's.

She wouldn't get into the car unless Tommy promised not to race the train, almost tearfully pleading - promising anything if he wouldn't make The Run. Too late. Even the thought of anything with Bonnie Sue didn't change his mind, though for a moment or two he had his doubts.

Tires squealing and defiance in his eyes

With his girl he had a fight

he cut out for the showdown as she cried,

"I know I'll grieve if you race this race tonight"

They were waiting for him, a dozen or so classmates, buddies and kids all lined up on the grass strip that lay between the road and the tracks of the mainline. Some of the kids, seeing the empty passenger seat, offered or begged to ride shotgun for this run for the record.

By 8:47 no sound akin to a train had been heard - the eight-three-eight was late! However, all was well and tension was relieved within a few minutes as the sound of number eight-three-eight, out of Wichita Falls, pierced the cool evening air. Without any discussion two of the spectator cars pulled onto the concrete blocking the highway so that no other vehicles could get in the way. Tommy moved the '51 to the point adjacent with the end of the guard rail, rapped the accelerator a few times and stared down the straight-away.

A little over a mile away the slightly curving tracks met and crossed the highway. All he had to do was beat the train to this point and he would again be top rodder at North Anderson High and surely Bonnie Sue's faith in his abilities would be returned.

The plume of thick gray smoke could be seen superimposed on the clear twilight sky from over a mile away and long before the west bound express itself was visible. Tommy raced the engine again and again wishing he had a tach to more accurately gauge the speed of

16

his mill. Some of the kids were jumping up and down with excitement. Delbert stood slack jawed and Johnny sat, wide eyed, glad it wasn't him this time.

The importance of the lateness of the eight-three-eight didn't register with Tommy as he readied himself for a good clean start. Glancing over his shoulder to the tracks he timed the dumping of the clutch to the exact moment the locomotive was even with him and the guard rail. The huge 4-6-4 iron monster, oblivious to its place in the destiny of that night, overshadowed the gathering of children playing with their toys.

Tires spinning, the little flathead strained in first gear, as the train roared by. A speed shift to second brought a chirp of rubber and Tommy felt a twinge of pride as the force of acceleration pushed him into the seat back. Just when it seemed that the engine was about to explode he power shifted into third. Now topping 70 miles per hour he dared a glance at the rushing sound to his right - the sound of a death knell?

Tommy was horrified to see that he was just now beginning to pass the speeding train. He was sure he should have been equal to the engine by now, but he was at least one car plus the tender behind. He pushed harder on the gas pedal and strained to hear if his engine had a miss or something. Ninety, 95, the needle swept past the 100 MPH mark and still he was not in front. The convergence, the intersection of death, was dead ahead. Where was the miscalculation? Did someone move the guard rail? Was the train running faster than its usual 60 MPH? Yeah! that's it. The train was late so they're running faster to make up for lost time. Flashing through his jumbled mind were thoughts of clamping on the binders and turning into the double barbed wire fence to his left - taunts of chicken - yellow - Bonnie Sue....

> He slammed the massive locomotive
> that was doin' better than 70 per
> and when they pulled him from the carnage
> his last thoughts were of her.

HOT ROD HERO

Old Style Wire Wheels

He hadn't been back to his old home town in over twenty years and then it was only for a funeral. The rolling hills of the asphalt interstate looked like the flat side of a giant blower belt cut and thrown casually across the beautiful south central Ohio farm land. He laughed to himself at his unintentional play on words; a blower belt draped around the "farm belt" of the nation. Crossing the county line, his county line, brought a flood of remembrances; memories of fun, simpler times and the race - the race for life. Where was it - the spot where the old road had been sliced by this modern highway?

Daydreaming was brought to a rapid halt by the sound of a siren attached to blue and red flashing lights. A quick glance at the speedometer confirmed his suspicions that it was he, for whom the sirens tolled. Swell. Welcome home hero. That's what you get for getting all melancholy while piloting a high powered sports car.

Down shifting his fully restored seventy-four, 454 Corvette he pulled to the side of the road adjacent to what appeared to be the remnants of an old two lane highway. The narrow strip of weed-sprouting black-top was now nothing more than a very long driveway for what looked like the south field to the Mulhouser farm. He wondered if any of the same family farmed it now.

"I've stopped you for exceeding the posted speed limit, sir. May I please see your operator's license," the Deputy Sheriff monotoned.

"I'm sorry officer. I guess I wasn't paying attention," he stated truthfully while searching his wallet - hoping that the license hadn't expired. "Is that the Mulhouser farm over there?" Nodding toward the fields of soybean, the Vette driver asked.

"Used to be. Fellah by the name of Krantz, from up around Columbus, owns it along with about three other farms around here. Absentee owner. Has a family by the name of, of...it'll come to me in a minute, tenant farming it now."

Handing the license to the officer he noted a slight pot belly contained by a sharply creased and neat shirt. This smart looking uniform was embellished with the standard polished brass accompaniments plus gold sergeant stripes. The deputy looked to be in his thirties though his graying hair could place him closer to forty. The neatly lettered name tag, Sgt. Vogt, jarred him. Might be, but Vogt was a common name in this area.

"You from these parts? Mr. Sampson."

"I was born and raised not far from the old Mulhouser place. Lived here till I went away to college. First time I've been back in twenty years," the Corvette man said. Remembrances of a young, dying mother bounced around in the combustion chambers of his mind like a broken connecting rod in a V8 engine - jagged edges tearing away pieces of the past.

He had been called a hero by some and a crazy fool by others. The county newspaper covered the incident with only a one quarter column saying they were afraid that publicity of that kind would only encourage others to ignore proper procedures.

After graduating from high school he had worked that summer, the summer of fifty-seven, on the Keaton farm. He, and the rest of the farm hands, had just taken a lunch break when the young and very pregnant kitchen helper, white as a sheet and holding a towel under her tummy, stumbled into the mud room.

Returning the driver's license the deputy asked, "Sampson. Seems I should know that name. You have any kin here?"

Blinking his eyes to snap back to the present he responded slowly, "Not any more. I was an only child, my mother died in seventy-two. My father lives with me."

"I'm not going to cite you, but I am going to run your VIN number through our computer," the officer said in his official tone as he copied the vehicle identification number onto his note pad. It'll only take a second or two if the system's up.

As the deputy turned toward his cruiser, Kent Sampson turned to the old stretch of blacktop and back four decades. "Help, please! I fell. I think I'm hemorrhaging!" The mother-to-be gasped as she surged into the kitchen. It only took Mr. Keaton a few seconds to sum up the situation. Knowing that the volunteer ambulance was at least 20 minutes away and the ride to the nearest hospital was over half an hour farther he looked to his young summer helper, "Son, will that hot rod of yours make it to the County Hospital over to Trenton any faster than ma old wagon?" The calmness of his employer strengthened him as he shook his head up and down stammering, "Yes sir, Yes sir."

"Well, bring it up here to the back door while the missus and I carry her out. The "missus", blood up to her elbows, was stuffing another towel between the neighbor's wife's legs all the while cooing a soothing message of all's well.

He remembered running to his rod with the only thought in his mind, did he have enough gas for a mercy run to the county seat in the next county over. He'd spent the past year building his pride and joy - a 1935 Ford, three-window coupe. He had, with the help of various hot rod magazine articles, chopped the top, channeled the body, dropped the front axle, installed a LaSalle transmission and hopped up a swapped engine.

He'd done his work well. The full race flat-head fired on the first crank of the starter. Twin pipes, grumbling through Glass-pacs, boosted his confidence as he slipped the tires gently across the gravel barn yard.

There was barely enough room for two, much less a pregnant woman in the altered coupe's tiny interior. As the missus packed towels, Mr. Keaton gripped his arm and in a low steady voice intoned, "Son, she may not pull through, but there's a chance you can save the baby. But you've got to step on it. I'll call over to the hospital and tell 'em you're ah comin'."

He spun gravel all the way to the blacktop, turned east and got on it hard barely getting into third gear before having to shut down for the first set of 'S' bends. Today, he realized, would be the test of his handiwork as he set the little coupe into the first sweeping turn. At the apex, inside front tire on the dirt berm, he poured the coal to the mighty Mercury flathead. The rear tires howled in protest as the power curve of the Clay-Smith cam let in all the fuel the over-sized pistons could suck through the polished ports.

There was no traffic and he used all of the roadway he dared. For the next few minutes his concentration was so intense that he hadn't had time to check his gauges much less the condition of his passenger. Just ahead loomed the narrow chicane, the right followed by a hard left, at the Mulhouser farm. This led to the only section of completed interstate in Spartan County. There he would have a chance to check everything.

Tires baying in dissent, young Kent brought his primer-red rod down to just under thirty-five from well above seventy for the first bend. He powered out of the final curve, tires squealing and engine screaming, to catch a glimpse of old mister Mulhouser out of the corner of his eye. The third generation farmer displayed his disgust at the speeding hot rod by shaking his fist at Kent from atop his John Deere.

Within minutes he was slamming the gear shift into high for the longest straight stretch of the run. Pleased at the sound of the three Stromberg ninety-sevens whooshing air through wide open butterflies he took the time to check the gauges. Oil: eighty pounds; temp: almost 200; fuel: cresting the empty mark; tach: 4200 and

21

climbing slowly; speedometer mounting steadily at 105. He looked to the little lady. Clutching her blood soaked towels; she forced a cringing smile that mocked her vacant stare.

One hundred and fifteen - one-twenty - one-twenty-two. The steering felt light and there was a pronounced vibration. He backed down to just under 120 and the vibration slackened. Water temp hovering at 210, he passed the new green sign: Trenton Exit - 5 miles. He was over half way there but, even at 120 miles per hour it felt extremely slow - time wise. Every attempt to go above 122 the vibration increased alarmingly. It must be those old wire wheels. He'd hand tightened each spoke and wire brushed them down to bare metal but still, true run-out was difficult to attain on those ancient wheels. He wished he'd had the money to buy new chrome-plated Dayton Wires or polished mags.

Drivers of the few cars he passed, at over twice their speed, stared wide-eyed and slack jawed at him. None dared to challenge him.

Slowing for the end of the divided highway gave him a final chance to study the interior. All okay except the temperature gauge. Maybe he had blown a head gasket which could, at these speeds, seize his perfectly rebuilt engine in short order. No question though, he would have to keep it floored.

After the zig-zag he ran a short straight tight in second gear and then had to double clutch down into first for the hairpin leading to the final set of 'S' bends. A quick glance at his passenger brought terror to his already over excited mind. Her head was listing at an unnatural angle, tongue visible and eyes half closed. He dared to take his hand from the wheel to shake her. "Lady. Lady," he screamed over the din of the high revving engine as he shook her near wrist. The entire arm flopped like an old heater hose. They were now down to minutes. He pushed the little copper wheeled coupe to its limit at each turn heading into the final straight. Here he'd have to open her up all the way, damn the temperature! Damn the vibration!

The newspaper reported that from the time the call was logged at the hospital to the minute the fender-less hot rod, smoke pouring from its hoodless engine, screeched to a halt at the back door of the emergency room only seventeen minutes had lapsed. The reporter believed it to be a mistake, but young tow-headed Kent Sampson knew better. The account further noted that Mrs. Vogt died in surgery but the premature baby boy was saved. The Vogt family called him a hero and named the boy James Kent in his honor. The doctor unequivocally stated that had they arrived only a few minutes later the child would not have survived. Contrarily, the police chief admonished his deed threatening to take him to jail if he ever did it again.

Sergeant Vogt jarred him into the present with the news that his Vette wasn't on the NCIC hot list. He had broken into a damp sweat, not for fear of the car being stolen, but from reliving the old memories.

Clearing his throat, "Say...ah, Sergeant, is your name, by any chance, James Kent Vogt?"

"Why no, but my little brother was James Kent. How could you know him?"

"Well, ah, I sort of met him once. Knew his mother too, but it was a long time ago. Whatever became of him?"

The officer stroked his chin while eyeing this stranger who was inquiring about his brother and a mother he never knew. "James Kent was a volunteer firefighter. He died a little over two years ago, saving a child from a burning building. Now how could you possibly know my mothe...OH MAN! The name didn't register until just now. Why, why, you're the kid...the hero, who drove a hot rod Ford from the old Keaton place to Trenton in seventeen minutes to save his life. Let me shake your hand Mr. KENT Sampson and say thanks, thanks very much."

Uncomfortable as it was, Kent twisted in his seat extending his hand for the obligatory grasp. "I'm sorry to learn of your brother's death...." After the brief awkward silence that imprisoned the grown men in their own revelations, Kent continued, "Whatever happened to the Keaton's, and that police chief and do you know what became of my coupe?"

"The last I saw of your car...say, my shifts almost up. Why don't you come on over to the house and we can catch you up on all these things. I'm sure my brother's family would like to meet you.

THE ASSIGNMENT

"Do you remember, William C . . . ? I do. It was your first command as a second louie, fresh out of OCS. The Captain had told you to take your men and secure the flank of Baker Company. You gathered the noncoms and soldiers, those who would have to traverse an open and muddy field from a tree line to a stone barn that housed at least one German machinegun.

"You told your troops, and these, William C, are the exact words: 'Men. You're not here to defend the life of your country; you're here to defend the life of the soldier next to you . . . because that's why he's here.' Do you remember that? I was very proud of your courage and leadership."

The old man, moving only his eyes, looked at the gray-headed, liver-spotted, 92 year old woman sitting bedside. But he saw only Becky, a suntanned honey with auburn hair and a smile that never left her piercing hazel eyes – the girl he married before going over-there. Their souls melded in the sixth grade when she asked him to the Sadie Hawkins Day dance. But, high school, sports and after school jobs only meant occasional and adolescent hellos and good-byes.

Less than a year into his first full time job - as lathe operator apprentice - his draft number came up. Reflecting on the importance of the letter that began, "Greetings," something compelled him to pay a visit to Becky's home, a modest, two-story, frame house with a low wraparound partially fenced porch on a street lined with towering Oaks. He showered and put on his graduation presents, a blue surge suit, white shirt and wide tie with bold red bands. Becky received him, barefoot and in a light yellow shirtwaist dress. She had high cheek bones, a few freckles and wore her auburn hair neatly trimmed below her shoulders.

The old man was William C, he never was called Bill, Billy or Willie or just plain William, it was always William C. Yes he remembered. And he also remembered something telling him to skirt the farm through the narrow drainage ditch – a place where he hoped the gunners couldn't see him. He glassed the area noticing at the edge of the plowed, bomb cratered field, a man in gray, baggy trousers and a large floppy, fedora type hat. Seemingly oblivious to the war, the man was harnessed to a plow while a woman in what must have been a skirt of lovely horizontal strips of red and green and blue, before being soiled by the mud, guided the plow. Maybe they were German scouts dressed to look like farmers. Maybe.

A frontal assault on the barn was what the Captain wanted, but William C worried that would cost a lot of lives and might not be successful. Instead he led a Sergeant and two riflemen, on their bellies through the oozing, cold muck to within fifty yards of the building. When the rest of his company opened up with covering fire, the BAR going, thump, thump, thump, he and the NCO jumped up and, emptied their carbines, zigzagging to the near wall.

Time almost stopped. It seemed like it took forever to insert a fresh magazine, rip a grenade from his shoulder, pull the pin, count three and toss. It looked to have hung in the air for what appeared to be – an inordinately long time - before finally arcing through the shot-out window in front of the machine-gunners. Crawling, sliding, rolling toward the barn door he was confused by a pain in his arm and upper leg – pain surrounded by dark red, muddy blood. He forced himself to stand, step around the door post, then drop and roll into the left side of the barn expecting the Sergeant to do the same for the right side. He came to the sitting position and again something told him to start firing to the left even before his eyes could adjust to the darkness. He shot, as tracers streaked from where an iron-wheeled tractor protruded from a darkened stall. Two Nazi soldiers dropped and three others threw up their hands. His NCO was still outside, shot through the head. The rest of the company, inspired by his leadership and those earlier words of encouragement, stormed the hay loft taking out a second machinegun emplacement and capturing additional enemy troops. The company received a Meritorious Unit Commendation . . . he gained a Purple Heart, the Silver Star and a silver bar.

At war's end there was little need for 1st Lieutenants with four battle stars, but he stayed three months into his first tour of duty in Korea when, during a blizzard, something told him to move left where he caught mortar fragments in his thigh. Perhaps if he had moved right or not moved at all, he would have caught the full force of the mortar. He never gave much thought to that inner voice that seemed to talk to him. He was not consciously aware of it, but something was there.

One rainy afternoon found him at a post matinee for the feature film, High Noon. Here, on his wedding day, the Town Marshall (played by Gary Cooper) learns that a man he sent to prison is returning on the noon train. The officer is torn between leaving on his honeymoon, as planned, or staying to face the threat. His bride (played by Grace Kelly) begs her groom to give it up. She leaves without him as Tex Ritter wails the theme song - the watchwords of police officers of all time:

> *"I do not know what fate awaits me,*
> *I only know I must be brave*
> *And I must face a man who hates me,*
> *Or lie a coward, a craven coward,*
> *Or lie a coward in my grave."*

26

The bride returns just in time to blow one of the gang members away to save her man, who then out-draws the ex-con. At that moment, William C realized that's what he wanted to do. Having experienced death in the war he fully recognized the reality that sometimes the bad guy wins and sometimes the spouse doesn't come back. But to a sworn law officer either one of those conditions was preferable than being labeled a craven coward. During this short reflective time, William C also realized he held a trait he believed most police officers had - a sixth sense. He always felt a subconscious and inborn ability to detect when to do or not do something of great importance – significant occasions such as that inner voice, the one that told him how to take out the enemy in the barn, to move left in Korea or calling on Becky. Either that or he had a guardian angel.

Deciding not to re-up, he applied to local police agencies, finally receiving an appointment as a deputy sheriff in and for his home county. He liked law enforcement work, finally becoming an instructor at the police academy after retiring as a Deputy Lieutenant.

William C and the barefoot girl in the yellow shirtwaist dress sat on the porch and between sips of iced tea in a lifetime measured in chills and short hot flares, they melded souls again. The Big Band music playing on a neighbor's Victrola filtered through open windows soothed their wispy and sometimes awkward conversation. He was not sure if the scratchy record was scratchy or if there was any street traffic as he only saw two hazel eyes and heard the concussion of bells superimposed on his mind. The lady named Becky stirred feelings of emotional splendor never imagined.

Perhaps it was the tea, or just destiny that caused strong and captivating interaction from the very first moment she came to the door. They fit together like a cushion to a couch or a long handled spoon to a tall glass of iced tea. Before the night ended, it seemed they were finishing each other's sentences - sometimes without even talking.

Sitting side-by-side and swaying gently in a swing designed for esoteric confidences they talked, laughed, bantered and oozed vibes far later than either were accustomed. Somewhere between the late night and early morning hours he told her, "This is fun and I really like being with you. The similarities are startling. The way you talk, look, laugh, well, ah," he stammered, examining his hands. "You really remind me of; let me count...my first wife. Yeah, that's it, wife number one."

> *That evening was magic as they*
> *talked and held hands,*
> *like life time lovers*
> *listening to modern day bands.*

He knew her mouth dropped open in indignation, but her voice was smiling. "Your first wife? How. . .how, many wives have you had?"

Keeping his eyes downcast, he took a sip of tea after which he slowly dabbed the napkin at the corners of his mouth. Then, still suppressing a grin, he touched the back of her hand with one finger, looked up, and matched her smile as he whispered, "None."

They married in the spring of 1942, their first child arriving a year to the day after that 'Day of Infamy.' Before Barbara Ann was a year old and with a second child on its way, he had already shipped out. William C got letters, postcards and a few photos, but he never saw, William C, Jr., his son – diphtheria, 1944.

William C struggled to raise up in the bed, to see the voice that had asked the questions and forced so many memories, but only Becky was there. She stroked his head and he succumbed to the soft pillow, the pain in his heart sharper even from such a slight exertion.

"You'll have a short energy boost when you can say your good-byes then you'll be with me and we'll see your mom and dad. They'll be like a mind's eye view of what you want them to look like – just as they will see you; as a baby, a child, in your uniforms, anyway they want whenever they want. And you'll meet William C, Jr. When the pain returns, let them give you the morphine as you'll be down to your last few hours. Then without pain and having to concentrate on what anyone is saying we can go over your assignment. There won't be much time as your grandnephew is going to be born next year."

The old man, aware of the pain in his chest, but free of it thanks to the morphine, closed his eyes, squeezed his bride's hand one last time and before he realized it - he was with the voice.

Looking down, he witnessed a nurse checking the battery of dials, gauges and life-monitoring gizmos attached to what had been . . .William C. He saw Becky tuck his hand under the sheet, the tears rolling down her cheeks.

"Thanks for watching over me all these years. And . . .well, I'm sorry I didn't pay better attention to what you were always trying to tell me."

The "voice," William C's great grandfather, who had died shortly before William C was born, replied; "As your grandnephew's guardian angel, I'm sure he will gain from your experiences and discernment."

BOOMERS AND 'BOS

Way car or Caboose

He wasn't sure he heard the first torpedo, but the second got his full attention and that of the locomotive engineer who pulled the throttle full back and yanked the whistle chain. Bartlett, fighting the deceleration, coupled with the coupled cars slamming into each other as the slack between them collapsed, strained to reach the window of the cab.

Number 4, a Santa Fe mixed-freight special east bound out of Needles, California, was highballing in high desert country when the emergency stop signals had gone off. He knew detonation caps placed on the track explode when crushed by the engine's wheels – a warning to immediately halt.

Just before the massive 2-10-2 mountain whaler, hissing a fog bank of steam, ground to a stop aside a red lantern, Bartlett caught a

30

glimpse of horses and riders. Highlighted by the massive headlamp he counted at least five with more movement fading into the deep black woods. As a Pinkerton man, he was purposely riding in the cab because the Wells Fargo car was heavy with a gold shipment. Specifically on the lookout for trouble he recognized the robbery routine at once.

The detective jumped from the off-side onto a steeply banked roadbed, pulling his five-inch barreled Colt from its holster. Fighting for footing in the loose rock and gravel he managed to stay in the steam cloud while scampering back to the opening between the tender and the first car. Before he could see the riders, he heard angry shouting from the old hogger, Tom Fiser – demanding to know who, why and what these men on horseback wanted. The answer came with multiple gun shots and the scream of the fireman – which was followed by a shotgun blast . . . and silence, save for the hissing and ticking of the 2-10-2.

Knowing that life might be over in a flash of gunpowder and wishing he had grabbed his Winchester before bailing out of the cab, Bartlett vaulted over the coupling between the cars shooting at the first rider he saw. Not waiting to learn of his marksmanship, the Pinkerton man wheeled and fanned at least three shots at other men on horseback now visibly painted by the light reflected from the steam. At least three because there were so many shots being fired he wasn't sure how many were his. But, he was sure one of these muzzle blasts caused his left arm to violently twitch. Bartlett tried to vault back over the coupling, but this left arm gave way and he crashed to the roadbed striking his head on the rail. Luckily his momentum carried him over the bed and down into the tumbleweeds and protection of the night.

An explosion ripped the air and produced a flash that silhouetted the entire train. These guys are good, he thought. They've shot the engineer and fireman fought off my return fire and blew the door off the money car in a very timely and precision manner. But how much time had elapsed?

Laying on the down slope of the raised roadbed, he knew his first priority was to reload. Even with the now searing pain in his left arm, he managed to eject the spent cartridges and stuff the cylinder with six fresh .32-20 rounds. Normally he only loaded five in the six shot single-action revolver as it wasn't safe to carry with the hammer down on a loaded round, but this was a firefight and not carry conditions.

Wide-eyed and ignoring the wound, he crept up the embankment fully expecting gunfire. Nothing. Dead quiet – even the engine. Had he passed out? Where is everyone – robbers, brakemen, Wells Fargo agents, horses? Staggering to his feet, he sought the safety of the engine and what light it provided hoping to retrieve his rifle. At the cab's ladder, using his good arm, he quietly climbed aboard. His rifle and ammo belt were as he left them, though he quickly realized with a bum arm the rifle would be of little use. The fireman, a boomer who was on his first trip firing for the S.F, lay across a pile of coal at such an odd angle it was clear he was dead. Tom, however, appeared to have propped himself up against the firebox, but looked slack jawed. Kneeling down, Bartlett could see the stain of blood on Tom's chest, surely a mortal wound.

He had met the hogman on a previous and uneventful run back in '98, when they were a little younger. They had gotten along well, neither man was married, but both had strong family ties and a formidable sense of fairness. Though Tom, ten years his senior was pushing 40 back then, they had bonded through discussions of family life and treatment of their fellow man. Their first meeting was one of Bartlett's early cases for the renowned Chicago based private detective agency. A thieving brakeman on Tom's train had been surreptitiously tightening select wheel brakes to cause hot boxes. When the conductor ordered the train onto a siding to investigate, the brakeman would slip into a loaded box car and throw out crates of freight to be picked up later by his gang. Bartlett suspected the rouse and was able to catch the crook in the act. That was the easy part. More difficult was tying the yard dicks into the act. The two railroad policemen had claimed they investigated the freight loss but couldn't explain it or catch the culprits. Bartlett, using various methods of, shall we say, persuasion, convinced the brakeman to tell how the S.F. cops were in on the thefts.

Not seeing any sign of the robbers from the vantage point of the cab windows, Bartlett untied the bandana from around the engineer's neck and wiped his friend's face while asking the obvious "how ya doin'" questions. The only response Tom could muster was a pleading look and a beckoning finger. Bartlett leaned close as the old hogger took a breath and whispered, "Will you see to it that my nephew, Thomas, gets my watch and what benefits the S.F.... ." He didn't finish as his eyes closed and his fingers relaxed.

No time for bereavement, he had to find the conductor and check the damage and inspect his own wound. Opening the firebox door for light, surprised that the fire was so low, he pulled his shirt off and stared at the bloody upper arm. Using the knife he always carried in his boot, he cut the good sleeve from his shirt and made a bandage as best he could. He was able to move his fingers and the arm, but only with intense pain.

Climbing back down, the first bodies he found were strangers – possibly robbers shot by him due to their proximity to the tender. Hoisting himself aboard the severely damaged W.F. car he found both agents had been blown into the next life by the blast that took the door off their car. The safe had also been dynamited, but Bartlett couldn't remember a second blast – or was this the only blast he heard? These were ruthless men.

"You all right mister?" The voice stunned Bartlett and he dropped, twisted and drew the Single Action Army revolver.

"Don't shoot. We're just bos. Bin ridin' in the empty hopper just aft o' this money car," the man dressed as an obvious hobo pleaded.

"How many are you? Where did the robbers go? Where's the conductor and brakemen?" Bartlett demanded, holstering his gun and jumping back to trackside.

The bo, terrified and flustered stammered, "You a rail dick?"

"Not likely. I work for Pinkerton. I'm not out to arrest, thump or toss you. Now, where are the others?"

"Back at the end, sir."

By the light of the caboose lanterns, Bartlett came upon an eerie scene that sent a chill through him – the conductor, brakeman and rear brakeman all lay shot dead while some of the hobos were rummaging through the trainmen's pockets. For the third time the detective drew his handgun as he ordered the bos to line up facing the way car.

Only after asserting they were just trying to get back the four bits each had paid the conductor to ride to Seligman, Bartlett holstered his .32-20. He then discovered there were a total of six men who, hidden in the hopper car, had escaped the slaughter of the robbers. They all had different opinions as to the direction the robbers departed. Additional questioning determined that two of the men were boomers. One, Johnson, a squat looking tough had been a brakeman for the U.P. and the other, Smitherman, a tall gangly kid, was a hostler who had just quit the Needles yard and hopped this special.

"Johnson, you're now the acting rear brakeman. Grab two torpedoes and the red lantern from the way car and protect the rear of this train. Do you know how to do it?" Bartlett ordered.

"Yeah. I jest go back 'bout a quarter mile an place the bombs on the track 'bout ten paces apart and set the lantern along side."

"Almost right. After you set the torpedoes, you stay there and wave the lantern at any approaching train. Don't come back until you hear our whistle. You got that?"

Turning to assume his task, Johnson mumbled a yes sir.

"Smitherman. Do you think you can move this train if one of these other men fire for you?"

"Yes sir." It was only this here morning that I built the fire in this here very engine and moved her onto the main line."

"Okay, I'm commandeering this train – I'm now the conductor and assume full responsibility. You there," Bartlett said pointing to one of the bos, come with me and Smitherman. You'll fire the engine. The rest of you men load the bodies into what's left of the Wells Fargo car and then you can ride the rest of the way into Seligman in the caboose." Almost as an afterthought, he added, "There's two more in the cab. They were all good men. Treat 'em with respect.

"Once at the station all of you are to stay in the way car until I say it's okay to leave. That means until after the Marshall in Seligman and I have had a chance to question you. That's an order."

As soon as steam pressure returned to the engine the crippled train and impromptu crew limped the remaining 40 or so miles into the station at Seligman, Arizona.

Bartlett S. Listner (he was never called Bart) had grown up along the Chicago and North Western Railway where his father's life ended in an all too common coupling accident. Pappy Listner, as he was known, was a good father and for as much as Bartlett knew, was a good husband too. Sometimes, though, even good guys die young. For the younger Listner, detective work was also an accident – that of being in the right place at the right time. His father, a C&NW brakeman, had gotten him a job as a call boy for the road. Bartlett's duty was to locate and notify boomers and others on the call board when needed to make a train. He seemed to have a natural ability to find people and the discretion when to not find them plus the physical grit to drag them in when necessary. On a day with a building snow storm he was able to round up, in a most timely manner, the required men to make up a special train. This special just happened to be for a Pinkerton operative who, recognizing Bartlett's abilities, immediately offered him a job.

Arriving at Seligman, the first thing Bartlett did, even before tending to his wounds and reporting to the Trainmaster, was to telegraph Pinkerton headquarters with a preliminary report. Finally, after all reports had been filed, the marshal notified and the men interrogated, he stopped by the barber shop to have his injuries tended. The bullet had passed through his upper arm, just chipping the bone. His head wound, which he now saw in a mirror, was ugly, covered in dried blood and would leave a nasty scar.

Hungry and tired, he took a room at the Harvey House Hotel. Here, after a few hours sleep, he cleaned up and settled into a back corner of the restaurant. Peggy, a vermillion haired Harvey Girl, was first to serve him. She remembered Bartlett as not only had their career paths crossed many times over the years, but they were from the same neighborhood. Their mothers had been friends. She was at least ten years older than Bartlett and had been a real looker – maybe even a dance hall girl – sometime in the nineties. Now, however, her figure gone and in a bland, food stained dress, she was just pudgy dumpy. Friendly, kind hearted, good at her job, a mother image for the other girls, but pudgy dumpy.

"Hi honey. Long time no see."

"Hello, Peggy. It's only been a month or so since I was here last. You doin' okay?"

"They keep me plenty busy. What can I getcha?"

While waiting for his food, he wrote a short note on the Harvey House postcards to his mother to let her know he was okay. With the release of the boomers and bos from the official investigation he was sure the story made front pages all across the nation and he didn't want her to worry. Sipping coffee after enjoying his steak and eggs, Smitherman the hostler/boomer, entered the room, looked around and when he saw Bartlett, headed straight toward him.

Without so much as a nod from the detective, Smitherman sat down and, in a low voice, revealed, "It really ain't none of my business, but ol' Tom Fiser was a friend o' mine." Looking around as if worried about his backside, he continued, "I seen three men in the Golden Spur Saloon ah woopin' it up. On the bar in front of them was a Well Fargo pouch – you know the kind they ship gold nuggets in."

"How many horses?"

"There were four tied up right in front of the Spur. But, I only seen three men at the bar."

Wow, this is a break. The robbers weren't even smart enough not to head to the train's destination. Seems these criminals had more dollars than sense. Bartlett thanked the man, paid his bill and kissed Peggy on the cheek before heading for the saloon.

Over confidence, not having a plan and being in a hurry can yield catastrophic events. Luck, however, can negate many such blunders. Bartlett's first mistake was of the self-assurance nature. The second was not securing the help of a posse or even the Marshall. He walked into the bar, stood directly behind the three men with the nugget pouch, drew his Colt and said in a commanding voice, "I'm Pinkerton detective Listner. You are all under arrest for robbery and murder. Place your hands on the bar."

The three men complied at once . . . the fourth – the one Bartlett failed to notice and sitting at a rear table placed his hands on a shotgun. The blast wounded two of the three robbers, but good guy Bartlett, who had not formulated a plan or waited for help, caught the mass of the charge. Like his father before him, sometimes even good guys die young.

FLATHEADS FOREVER

1949 Ford

Drivin' hard or cruisin' slow

Grab that shift lever

And never let 'er go

Flatheads are forever

"Two-hundred-forty-nine bucks for a '49 is a bargain you shouldn't let pass. I knew the matronly lady who bought it new and always had it serviced. Where else can you find such a deal for two-forty-nine for a really clean, and I mean a no rust Ford convertible - it's got... ."

"Whoa, wait a minute," Chris interrupted the non-stop monologue of the used car salesman. You don't have to sell me, as soon as I raise the money, this is the car I want. How 'bout if I give you fifty now and you hold it for me until I can earn the rest?"

Hyped up for his first car, seventeen year old Chris was oblivious to the engine miss and sounds of brake shoe metal on metal during the obligatory test drive. He had yearned for a Ford convertible since his uncle had taken him for a ride in just such a car in 1949 when Chris was only ten years old. Now, five years later, Chris had his dream car.

With his elbow on the door sill and hand on the cozy wing post, top flopped, ducktails swirling in the backdraft and sporting a set of aviator style shades, Chris Waterbaker was the epitome of cool. The first stop, after a cruise-by, was the Bun Boy on Dixie Highway. Pulling into one of the car-hop slots, Timmy Verdun, his best buddy, shuffling in his engineer boots, sauntered over from his '51 Chevy that had been nosed and decked.

"Hey man, I see ya finally got that forty-niner. What are you gonna do to it?"

"First I'm going to build the engine so it will dust off a Caddy or two. Then, maybe pull a few trophies at the strip, then... ."

"Hop up the engine? You don't know Jack Shit . . . ," Timmy exclaimed.

Looking playfully hurt, Chris said, "Come on man, I do so know Jack. I've known him for years."

Catching the drift of the joking, Timmy challenged, "If you know Jack Shit, what kind of car does he drive?"

"He's runnin' an Eighty-eight Olds," Chris played along.

"Naw, man. See, I told you, you don't know him. Jack wouldn't be caught dead in an Olds," Timmy said as he playfully punched his buddy in the arm.

The two young men had grown up on the same street and played, roughhoused and matured together while always tinkering with mechanical things. At twelve, they built a jitney using baby buggy springs and wheels and scrap wood scrounged from wherever they found it. Though it wasn't exactly a 'custom' or a 'hot-rod' Timmy exhibited his bodywork talents in shaping a streamlined cover for the used lawnmower engine traded for by raking leaves for a neighbor who had purchased a replacement mower.

Chris was the engineer who not only disassembled and successfully reassembled the one-lunger, but milled the flat-head with a hand file to increase the compression ration. Wanting more power, he decided he needed a full-race cam. Having read about hi-lift cams in various car magazines, Chris, using a grinding wheel on a quarter-inch electric drill, ground down the base of each lobe on the cam and had a local welding shop weld a little metal onto the ends of each valve which he then ground to the correct clearance. Not realizing he needed to fly-cut the head to compensate for the mill job and higher lift of the valves, the aluminum head cracked the first time he yanked on the starter rope.

Upon reaching driving age and securing a part time job at Buops Texaco, Timmy was first to buy a set of wheels, a 1951 two-door Chevrolet. He removed the hood and trunk chrome and, using the station's torch, leaded in the holes.

Chris had hired on for an after-school job with the local box factory, bailing scrap corrugated paperboard. As soon as he accumulated the funds, it was back to the used car lot where he claimed the '49. Using his parents attached garage the first day of summer vacation, Chris, with Timmy's help, removed the Miami Cream colored hood to make work on the engine easier. Next to come off was the Ford-Holly '94' carburetor and then the distributor, plug wires and anything else that was going to get in the way of pulling the heads. To make it easy, Chris loosened all the bolts holding the head, and then used the starting motor to turn the engine over to create pressure in the combustion chambers. With the loose head bolts, the heads popped free. A trick he read about in Car Craft magazine.

> Wrist pin connected to the piston
> Connecting rod connected to the wrist pin
> Crank shaft connected to the connecting rod
> All connect for a pleasing din

Chris was big for a high school junior, not tall, or bulky, just big as in muscular and strong. He'd only been in one real fight, but that battle established him as tough, even though he was scared – not of being hurt, but of not actually engaging in the fight and thus being labeled chicken. The incident began when a senior, who was at least as big as Chris, called him a girly because of his wavy chicken-yellow hair. The kid taunted him until Chris got into the senior's face, and not knowing what to do, snarled. He growled like a dog and bared his teeth. There were a bunch of other kids standing around the lunchroom water fountain who went silent at this confrontation.

Chris sensed that if the senior backed down, he, Chris, might be forever called chicken-yellow or worse. In only an instant, the senior twisted quick and hard jamming his shoulder into Chris' chest perhaps in an attempt to get out of a fight. And then the dukes sailed, whizzed, flew and connected. Neither boy had had any fisticuff training, thus they flailed at each other until both had bloody noses and sore knuckles. The winner was the gym teacher when he separated the two who were then made to shake hands. The senior was also his rival for Kathleen, the pert sophomore cheerleader with a coy smile – a downcast, eyes up look she used when coming on to guys she liked. She witnessed the fight, but stormed out of the lunchroom when the gym teacher jumped in.

Looking at the stripped block, Timmy said, "Tell me again why you want a flathead?"

"Ever since my Uncle Sy took me for a ride in his, then new, forty-nine, I've wanted one just like it. Uncle Sy not only had a cool ragtop, but he also raced a quarter midget with a V8 60 flathead on dirt and board tracks."

"Hey, I didn't know that. How come I never met this cat?

"Cause, he's dead. He ran at tracks all over the country and finally, one Friday night at the Cincinnati Race Bowl, a high-banked quarter mile track, the ol' number three spun out and he was creamed by another car. This was about four years ago."

"What happened to the cars?"

The sixty powered midget was totaled and my aunt sold the forty-nine."

With the heads off, Timmy and Chris inspected the cylinders and valves only to discover deep scores in the walls. "Ah man," Chris moaned, "We're gonna have to pull the engine and have the block bored. I ought to find that salesman and pound his face – matronly lady and always serviced . . . I'll bet the oil wasn't changed until they put it on the lot."

"Well, the good news is you'll have more cubes," Timmy chipped in trying to make the best of the situation.

For the rest of the summer, between working for the box factory that put him on full time until school started in the fall, and chasing after Kathleen, he found some time to work on his rod.

If it was anything he learned that summer, it was he didn't want to work in a factory. The box plant produced corrugated containers – the corrugated board being formed with steam to cook the starch that was used as a glue to cement the medium, the fluted part, to the front and back liners. On days when the outside temperature rose into the nineties, and even with all the factory windows open, it could get hotter than the headers on an alcohol fueled dragster.

Waiting for the block to be bored sixty thousands over at the C&J Machine Shop, Chris socked away his pay check to cover the expense of new pistons, rings, bearings and speed equipment. So as not to look completely stock, he installed a set of lowering blocks and used fender skirts. The skirts were Bayview Blue, but Chris sanded off the paint and Timmy spray painted them Miami Cream to match the body color.

As soon as he got the engine block out of hock, he immediately set to work modifying it. Using a power drill and grinding wheels, he carefully ported and polished the intake ports. Next he relieved the block by grinding away excess metal between the valve opening and the cylinder. It was slow going, usually one cylinder or port per day. But when he finished, the finishes were smooth as Kathleen's . . . well as smooth as he could imagine. The machine shop had also ground and reseated the valves which rode on adjustable lifters that followed the lobes of a full race Clay-Smith cam.

Timmy stopped by when his work schedule allowed – work for pay at Buop's and work on his rapidly progressing custom. He had leaded in the door handles and installed a solenoid to open the doors via a push-button switch hidden under the front wheel well. The body was still spotted primer awaiting his next chore – chopping the top.

Chris did manage a few dates with Kathleen when his father allowed him to borrow the family stagecoach, a 1955 Chevy Nomad. It was powered by the new V8 with Power Pack, but that was coupled to a Powerglide tranny and thus very slow off the line. Once he brought Kathleen over to show her the forty-nine, but she couldn't believe he – or anyone – could put it back together again.

> *Camshaft lifts the lifters*
> *Fly-wheel spins the clutch disk*
> *Ring gear twists the axle*
> *Throttle up and take the risk*

On a Saturday night, late in August, both boys reinstalled the short block which also included a lightened flywheel and truck clutch he bought at the junk yard. By the next Sunday, with Timmy in his chopped custom '51 as the possible tow vehicle, they headed for the strip. The first run, he fishtailed off the line, had to back off, but turned a respectable 89.6. During the second run of the preliminary drags, the axle broke and Timmy had to tow him home.

The following Sunday, it was back to the strip with a junk yard axle, only this time the universal joints came apart on the first run. The word in the pits was Chris might have more power than the car can handle. Chris really wanted a trophy and the third time must be the charm. On the successive Sunday, he qualified, dusted off another flathead and then during the trophy run the drive shaft snapped. And so the drag season ended.

Though the hopped-up engine wasn't made for back and forth to school trips, it was fun and all the kids recognized the sound of Chris' dual piped, Smitty's mufflers. Chris knew he couldn't keep the forty-nine when he headed off to college, so he planned to trade for a '53 Ford sedan - a stocker. He realized he could afford to buy a new '56, but he wanted to own the last of the flatheads.

Summer 1956 promised to be the time for graduation, stacks of trophies and fun. The reality was his mother took sick and Chris had to put in a lot of overtime plus take care of his younger brother and sisters. Spare time was spent with Kathleen, mostly helping her help her invalid grandparents – and maybe a movie or two – especially Giant, which they saw twice.

September: end of summer, end of teen hot rodding, end of romance? Chris had one last chance to garner a trophy. He checked everything twice, wiped down the oxidized and faded Miami Cream paint with motor oil to make it shine and used his bicycle pump to add extra air to the front tires . . . and with Kathleen snuggled beside him to do the shifting, off they went to the strip.

D-Gas that day contained a few hot machines, but Chris was convinced if he could keep from breaking anything, he could win. He got through the preliminaries with ease and then came up against a fifty-five Chevy with a set of quads. In first gear he spun the tires a little too much and the Chevy moved out. But second gear, with the Clay-Smith cam allowing the over-sized pistons to suck huge amounts of air through the polished and enlarged ports from the six-deuces, the forty-nine pulled even at the half way point. A slam shift into third brought a chirp of rubber and the Chevy was a distant second at the end of the quarter mile. Chris had his trophy.

Six-Deuces

At the strip that glorious day

his D-Gas coupe turned in eighty-nine, nine.

But elation was nothing compared

to seeing her in the spectator line.

Carrying the wood and metal prize from the announcer's stand back to the pits, Timmy caught up with him, put his arm over his buddy's shoulder and grinned, "I guess you really do know Jack . . . he drives a forty-nine with a full race flathead."

EXIT TO MAIN STREET

"Come on honey, let's check it out. We've got plenty of time."

"Ah, Sugar, we have enough antiques and junk, besides this place looks like an antique itself. Just in case, and if we have a good signal strength out here in the boonies, I'll call the inn and make sure no one worries if we run a little late. . .ahh, yes, four bars."

Honey and Sugar Elmore, driving through the small northeastern village of Bakeville, near the borders of Vermont and New Hampshire were en route to a private resort two towns further west. It was in the early twilight of a late summer rainy day 2015, and they were running right on time. The destination was to be a family reunion with their adult children and grandkids, some coming from as far away as Texas.

Reluctantly, Honey pulled to the curb on Main Street, just past a brick furniture store advertising 50% off every item on all three floors. Encompassed as part of the furniture store's façade, on this the north side of Main Street, was a laundromat, then a shoe repair shop and finally, at the corner, a free-standing bank building. East of the furniture store was a parking lot. The brick building was most likely built mid-20th Century while the bank looked to be of very recent and modern construction. On the other side of the street, in the haze of the humid light filtering through massive American Elm trees, was a lone slightly dilapidated, clapboard, two-story cape-cod style house with a bright sign saying: 'Unique Antique, Come in for a new view.' The sign didn't seem lighted or florescent, just strangely bright. Due to the misty weather and foliage surrounding the house, it appeared to be a small single-family home common to the area, but from a different era.

It was the sign that caught Sugar's attention. She wasn't looking for anything, just enjoying the scenery and ride in their recently restored 1948 Ford station wagon – the one that was still made of wood, except for the fenders. In 2005, as a fun project, Honey and Sugar had bought the worn-out, and dry-rotted car. Working evenings and weekends, it took them ten years to complete the restoration. Honey had learned mechanics and woodworking from his father, a cabinet maker; Sugar, while still a teen-ager, had discovered the intricacies of leather seats from helping her mother fabricate slipcovers to make ends meet after her father passed away.

Honey, aka Wendell Wilford, had recently retired after 32 years as a plant manager for a label manufacturer. Before that, he was a pressman for the offset lithographing company that printed the labels. He didn't just supervise the making of labels, but the very special labels for whisky bottles. The whiskey industry was very particular about the image projected by the bottle's shape, size, heft and especially the label. Labels that might include die cutting, embossing, gold bronze and multiple colors also required hand sorting to make sure no out-of-register marques of these exquisite spirits ended up on a bottle.

Priscilla, called Sugar since she was old enough to know she hated her given name, spent her working years as an illustrator for one of the top clothing fashion designers. Both had met at Miami (of Ohio) and instantly took a mutual liking to each other. They married in their senior year.

Sugar was very sensitive, yet inquisitive which often conflicted with her life. For example, Sugar could sense danger, but her need to investigate sometimes brought consequences such as the time she felt something was wrong with the way a shop clerk was acting. Instead of calling the police, she barged into the store office to find a thug holding a gun on the owner. This incident turned out okay, like the premonition she had about their forth born. She babied the baby of the family, but couldn't shake the dread that gripped her heart. Just before his third birthday, the red-headed tyke with a perpetual mischievous smirk, contracted Reye's Syndrome, which was misdiagnosed. Sugar intuitively believed the diagnosis was wrong and beseeched the doctors until proper treatment was activated. Helpless and facing the boys fatal condition, she, Honey and their eldest daughter, Bethany, took turns holding him around the clock until he, miraculously, began to show signs of improvement.

Their remaining family of two boys and a girl had produced, so far, six grandchildren and to them, life had never been so good. Now, this scattered clan was going to be together for a full week high in the Green Mountains of Vermont.

The sign seemed out of place for a place that was a faded yellowish orange with paint-pealed window shutters that hung askew from the upper story. A slightly wobbly looking picket fence, mostly covered with vines and ivy, was the same color as the building and wrapped around this, six-rooms at most, town house.

Honey, catering to Sugar's whim, set the emergency brake and closed the cowl vent as sometimes it leaked during heavy rain. Crossing the street they noticed the notice asking visitors to use the alley side entrance to this corner lot house. Turning the corner into the narrow alley, the side door looked farther away than it should be for such a small home. At the break in the fence, Honey looked back toward the intersection but it was obscured. He couldn't see the bank building, their car or the street sign – must be the foggy mist. Approaching the only visible door, both were surprised to feel a chill as it opened just as Honey raised his hand to knock. Stepping into an open space with what looked to be larger than this diminutive house, they faced a single frosted and pebbled glass door framed in dark wood. Lettered in gold-leaf on the glass were the numbers 1942. Above the door was an open transom though no sound emanated.

The front door closed behind them and now the only light came through the frosted glass door and its transom. Shrugging their shoulders, Honey and Sugar opened the door and were immediately greeted by a young woman in a smartly creased kaki uniform with the silver bars of a 1st Lieutenant on her shoulders. This was in contrast to Sugar's low-rise, bare-midriff, stretch pants and halter top and Honey's boot-cut, Levis and polo shirt. The room's walls were covered in World War II patriotic posters and recruiting slogans. Each of the many tables was covered with paper stacks, in/out boxes, and noisy typewriters manned by uniformed soldiers busy at work. The Lieutenant, smiled and said, "If you're here to sign-up, I can help you. Where did you get such clothing? I've never seen anything quite like it. But, don't worry if you can't afford good clothes, the Army will dress you proper."

Mystified to the point of being speechless, they started toward two frosted and pebbled glass doors at the far end of the room; one lettered, 1890, the other; Exit to Main Street. "No, we're just looking," Honey replied. Honey whispered to Sugar as they passed the final desk, "Isn't this the strangest thing ever. It feels just like we stepped back into our parent's era? Let's get out of here."

"No, I've got to see what's in this 1890 room," Sugar said, stepping through the door - a chill was felt while the clacking of the typewriters suddenly ceased. Honey turned to look back, but all he saw was a blank space.

Honey and Sugar found themselves, not in a room, but on a trolley car, a trolley car pulled by two massive brown horses. Seated were a few women dressed in long full dresses with collars uptight to their necks and hats on piled-high hair. They were clutching a sign that read, 'Lips that touch liquor shall not touch ours'. The men, some wearing bibbers and working men's caps sat next to gentlemen with handlebar moustaches and long sideburns. The windows were steamed, but Sugar caught a glimpse of a man on a bicycle – the type with the enormous front wheel - and a wooden sidewalk in front of a bar fronting a huge sign advertising bratwurst and beer.

The conductor began walking through the car collecting fares. When he got to Sugar and Honey, he seemed aghast at their attire, but nonetheless demanded the fare of five cents each. Honey, produced what was easiest, his money clip; pulled a dollar bill and handed it to the man with the short stove-pipe, brimmed cap. The conductor examined the bill and exclaimed in a loud voice, "What is this? Are you trying to pass some counterfeit money? We'll have none of this. Get off my car or I'll hail the coppers!"

Scared, worried and almost panic stricken the Elmore's hastened to the doors marked, Exit to Main Street and 1922. As Sugar reached for the Main street door handle, the trolley rolled over a set of uneven railroad tracks causing her and Honey to push through the entrance to 1922 and into a young lady in a flapper style above-the-knee skirt, short hair and a long string of pearls around her neck. She was smoking a cigarette affixed to an extended holder that was tipped in silver.

"Well aren't you the cat's meow. Where'ja get them pajamas and you can't bring your cakie in here without a tie. This ain't no gin joint," she cracked, obviously well inebriated.

"What time is it, Honey, Sugar begged, scanning the room for the Exit to Main Street sign. Honey fished his smart phone from his pocket and pushed to activate. The flapper, said, "What's that big boy?"

"It's a phone and . . . and there's no signal."

"You mean telephone. Come on, that ain't no telly-phone, it ain't got no wire. Let's you and me have a little drinky-poo."

Seeking the sought-after escape sign through the smoky din of what was clearly a speak-easy, Honey and Sugar worked their way through a jazz dancing crowd to the escape door, and this time they made it through the one marked, Exit to Main Street. Staggering onto the sidewalk of a strange and unsettling setting, they were baffled again.

Parked in the alley was a Ford vehicle, but a model that was unfamiliar. Stunned and confused, Sugar smiled and said, "We might have gone through the wrong door and slipped into the future, but they still have license plates on this, this whatever it is." She stooped down to read the plate, then looked up at Honey, "It

49

says the plate expires in May . . . twenty-twenty." Without a word, both began walking through the hazy mist, but when they were close enough to read the street sign, the sun was shining.

Though the sign clearly displayed Main Street, nothing was the same. The bank was still there, but weathered and rundown – and closed. The brick furniture building with the shops was now a twenty story hotel. Their pride and joy, the 1948 restored Ford Woody – gone as was the sign in front of a small and now very dilapidated, clapboard, two-story cape-cod style house.

Honey at once snatched his smart phone from his hip pocket and called Bethany who lived in upstate New York, just a few hours away.

"Hi Beth . . . it's dad."

"Dad? Dad who? Where are you? Is this a joke?"

"No. it's really you father and mom is with me. We're okay, but we can't find our car."

"Your car? We searched for you. Where have you been? It's been five years. We had your car towed. Where… ."

"Listen, Beth, my battery is low, we'll tell you all about it. Can you come and pick us up? We're still in the same town. We'll be in the Bakeville Hotel, right where the Woody was parked."

The Elmore's entered the Bakeville Hotel and inquired of the desk clerk for a room to freshen up. With no luggage and an expired Visa card they had to pay cash, for which the key was reluctantly tendered. Exiting the elevator on the 20th floor, they found the room, inserted the key and walked into 2065.

Bethany and her husband, Jason, upon arriving in Bakeville were unable to locate the Bakeville Hotel or any hotel. She immediately pressed reconnect for the last incoming call only to hear, "We're sorry, your call cannot be completed as entered or the number has been disconnected."

A middle age couple, unseen and not properly dressed for a funeral, stood at the rear of the crowd and were the last to leave. The man, wearing jeans and a polo shirt, pulled from his pocket a technologically obsolete cell phone and placed it on the headstone. The woman bent down and ran her fingers over the chiseled inscription: Bethany Wilford Blevins, 1985-2065.

THE PICK-UP

1937 Ford Pick-up truck

From some quarry deep in Wisconsin, via cavernous ships, came the iron ore. Compounded, mixed and incorporated with other raw ingredients from mines as far away as the continent of Africa; the River Rouge's open hearth furnaces formed the very heart of America's rolling stock. But it took the conscientious and loving care of the meticulous assembly line workers to collate these unique organs and create the real soul of each vehicle.

Early in January, 1937, number 3846, a pick-up truck, received its "soul". She came down the line and under the tender guardianship of the day shift, was bestowed the larger 85 horsepower V8 engine, Vermillion Red paint with black stripe and black "solid" wheels.

I felt good and rode proud and tall on the train to St. Louis where an elderly gentleman gently drove me to the show room at the Ford dealership just west of downtown. I didn't have to wait long, like the plainer coupes and sedans, some of which had to remain out in the rain and cold. On January 22, Number 3846, that's me, became the property of Mr. Silas T. Wentworth, a lanky and muscular farmer from up-state Missouri.

Silas T., his wife, Priscilla, and their son, Jamie, took pride in their first "new" car. The depression had been difficult but through hard work and very austere living they prospered. I heard Silas T. talking about how I, as their new addition to the family, would enable him to increase his market deliveries three fold over the horse and wagon.

Even hauling hogs to market was no strain for my powerful flathead engine, and return trips, empty except for a few supplies, made life easy and enjoyable. Mr. Wentworth. changed my oil and greased me on a very regular basis and Jamie kept me clean. The missus even made seat covers for me.

Things changed in 1940. Jamie turned 16 and began driving me to school and other places. Silas T. bought a heavy duty, dual-rear-wheel truck that soon became the pride of the family. Jamie was hard on me with all his quick starts and fast driving, but I knew I was having a better life than some of the others I'd see stuck by the roadway or - in junk yards! Once, when we went to town, I saw a sedan that had been right behind me on the assembly line. That sedan was now a police car with a spot light and a two-tone paint job. And, even though she was just a sedan, she turned up her nose at common pick-ups.

Jamie had a special girl and they often went out for rides together, only they spent more time parking than actually riding. They talked of marriage and how he was sure his dad would give him the pick-up and sign on a note so as he could buy the old Potter place.

We had a lot of fun, the three of us. Jamie and I once raced a Chevrolet out on the East River Road. We sprayed gravel all over that snooty looking Chevy, and doing almost 90, beat him by a country mile! Mabel, that's his girl, made him promise never to do that again because they would need me for farm use.

It was in my bed, on blanket covered straw, during the summer of 1942, they got engaged. Mabel was scared but Jamie promised to love her forever. They talked about the kids they wanted and how they would fix up the old Potter place, even a stall in the barn for me, when he got back.

It all seemed so perfect except that I was getting tired and one of my springs was starting to sag a little. Jamie sure looked sharp in that uniform with all those shiny buttons. I don't know why everyone was crying, even Mabel. The two men drove me to town. They shook hands, hugged, and Jamie patted me on my fender before he got into a bus. Silas T. brought me back, parked me in the lean-to where the surrey used to be, and disconnected my battery.

It was a long time before anyone opened that barn door again. Silas T. Wentworth, on that cold and windy day, looked gaunt and sad. A plump pimply faced kid, Mr. Wentworth called him Butch, kicked my tires, shook my fenders and looked me over then handed my first master a check. The next day Butch returned, winched me onto a trailer, and took me back into the big city.

Much to my surprise Butch began cleaning me and showing me off to his friends who came to visit the garage. It seems the garage is the headquarters for the Piston Busters Car Club. It wasn't long before Butch and friends had yanked my old and tired engine and with a little drilling, grinding and welding - the welding hurt - installed an almost new Corvette engine! Wow! Butch sanded off the old faded paint and applied a bright yellow primer, converted to hydraulic brakes and added fancy chrome wheels with new white-wall tires. Boy, if only my old assembly line mates could see me now! I'll bet even the police car would be envious.

Every time we went to the Big Boy drive-in all the other guys would gather around and admire me. Sundays, we'd go to the drag strip, and though it pained me to have that much pressure put on my rails, I loved it. Sometimes we even brought home a trophy! The speeds we reached were far more than Jamie and I had ever dreamed. Things weren't all that great though. A few of my body mounts were wearing out and the high output V8 engine, twisting against my rusty frame, gave me a lot of twinges. I was sure that someday I wouldn't be able to keep it together.

Other than that, life was pretty good - at least I didn't have to haul any smelly ol' hogs or dusty hay. But I did carry a few kegs of beer and a bunch of club members more than once. Butch always kept me in a garage and never let anyone else drive me, 'cept Carrie, his girl, and that was only on one occasion.

Late in the spring of '60 we were coming out of a high speed turn on the new subdivision road when one of my shock mounts broke. It caused me to lose control and we slammed into a stone wall bending my front axle and crumpling one fender. Butch broke my windshield with his head and leaked a sticky red oil all over my cowl and hood. He lay there for a long time before one of those stuck-up police cars and a shiny new ambulance arrived. Then things happened pretty fast and next thing I know they tow me to, of all places, a junk yard!

With a half century's worth of the formerly new and proud modes of transportation to trade stories with, I was never lonely. And though I was not happy with my situation at least I had had a more complete and exciting life than most of the other "junkers". But, I still had a lot of life left in me and I didn't want to spend forever with these rusty heaps.

Oh, sometimes somebody would come and look me over - shake me or kick my now flat tires, but mostly they just wanted my parts. As the years rolled by I lost my steering wheel, the good front fender, my radiator, engine - it was only a Chevy - and other items. My interior rotted away and the faded yellow primer - Butch never did get around to that metal flake paint job he had promised - rusted through in many places. At least I had the other cars to keep me company not like being shut in the Wentworth barn all alone. A once majestic LaSalle, the leader of the yard, because of the shade from a Maple tree that grew out of his trunk, became my best friend. He loved to tell of the times he chauffeured the Mayor and his important guests and friends around.

Sometimes you get lucky. I had never resigned myself to the junk yard mentality of my fellow prisoners as I always believed I'd be rescued. It was hot, late in the fall of 1989, when I winked a goodby to the huge LaSalle. Norm, a jovial man who looked to be almost as old as Silas T. had looked the last time I saw him, carefully loaded me onto a trailer.

My next home was, well, better than the factory. It was clean, brightly lighted and had some very sophisticated tools and machinery. I just knew Norm and I were going be the best of friends. It took over two years, but in that time I was reborn! Even my assembly line mates would hardly recognize me. Normie - that's what his wife calls him - took me all apart, I mean every nut, bolt, flange, bushing - everything. He stripped my metal bare and then what he didn't primer and paint he chromed. I also received new fiberglass fenders, a new dropped front axle, a chopped top - it only hurt a little - rolled & pleated naugahyde interior and - ugh - another Chevy engine, but complete with supercharger. I loved it. I wanted to go by the junk yard and show-off.

In no time at all Normie sold me to a man who I'm ashamed to identify. A man whose smile never reaches his eyes. Almost every weekend he loads me into a closed trailer and tows me to a car show. He ropes me off so none of the countless admirers can caress my 27 hand-rubbed coats of lacquer or fondle my cute little stainless and wood steering wheel. Ah, this should be the life, no more hauling of any kind, frame stressing races or even getting rained on. Only trouble is I hate it. My engine, even though it's not a Ford, has never been started. Once when he had me sitting in his driveway a few of his friends came by in "real" hot-rods with engines that worked - I was so embarrassed. I long for just sitting at a Big Boy and maybe a few wheel spins in the lot, the wind at 100 per or the pleasure of a master who knows how to handle a street rod.

Say...if you see me at one of those frilly, trailer-queen, car shows, make my owner an offer he can't refuse, put some guts in my mill and let's do it! I won't let you down.

FLASHING BLUE LIGHTS

2015 JACK PUMPHREY

1975 Ford

The first shot tore through his upper leg exiting just below the hip.
The second and third shot hit... .

He lay on the extra firm, queen sized mattress under a sheet and light wool blanket listening to the sounds of the city. The bike ride had helped but he still felt itchy. It was almost midnight, and all he had done for the last hour was stare at the dancing lights on the ceiling. Somewhere close by emergency vehicles' sirens wailed and yelped. They passed his apartment causing the beacons – the blue flashing beacons – to play tag with the other lights that bounced off his ceiling, walls and mirrors. The tough ex-cop/private detective/motorcycle rider closed his eyes and fought the twenty some-odd-year old nightmare... .

Keying the mic and activating the roof lights all with one movement, Sergeant Travis Tarvon calmly gave his car number, "Four-John- Eleven."

"4-John -11," the dispatcher echoed.

"Possible DUI, farm-to-market, four-three-two, four miles west of eight-twenty-one. Older model Ford sedan, blue in color, bears Texas Tom-Adam-Sam-nine-nine-eight."

"Eight-William-Eight. Car 8-William-8."

"8-William-8."

"8-William-8 are you clear on 4-John-11's location? Possible DUI?"

"Affirmative. I'm south bound eight-twenty-one. Be about fifteen."

A jack rabbit, highlighted by the headlights of both vehicles, scampered across the highway as the patrol car's spotlight lit up the interior of the losermobile. The blue flashing lights were swallowed in the pitch black of the West Texas prairie. In the grimy Ford he could see three subjects, two males and a female. The driver slowed and put two wheels on the gravel shoulder kicking up a cloud of dust. Nobody was making any frantic moves like they were trying to hide contraband or weapons. It looked like a routine stop.

Just before exiting his car the radio broke squelch, "4-John-11, no wants NCIC, Texas Tom-Adam-Sam-nine-nine-eight."

"4-John-11 okay. 2-7."

"2-7, 4-John-11. Oh-one-forty-four hours. KQA-two-three-oh."

At the open window, the experienced officer noted the distinct odor of alcoholic beverage on the driver's breath and a half empty whiskey bottle on the back seat. The occupants, dirty, scruffy and smelly all appeared to be in their thirties. The female, in a tube top and seated in the shotgun seat, seemed to be spaced out. The small framed back seat passenger watched with intense but dilated eyes.

"I'm stopping you, sir, because you drove off the road in two places back there. May I see your operator's license, please," Travis commanded in a firm but polite tone.

The man with a two day's growth of beard said his name was Tom Hickey. After a few minutes of fumbling in his wallet and scattering the contents of the glove box all over the front seat, he claimed he couldn't find his license or registration. "You're going to have to step out of the car, sir," Travis said, opening the driver's door while trying to watch everybody's hands at once.

He led the man, who was about his size, to the rear of the cruiser and well out of view of the passengers. Travis ran the driver through a series of divided-skills evaluations and horizontal gaze nystagmus for documentation purposes in case of a contested court hearing. The Sergeant had an uneasy feeling. This man was more than just drunk. He could have stalled until his back-up arrived, but he felt if he could just put the cuffs on him, he and the others would be easier to control. "I'm going to have to arrest you for driving under the influence."

"Aw, c'mon man. I can handle it. You've seen worse. C'mon let me go," Hickey whined.

With a sigh of capitulation, the arrestee turned to place his hands on the trunk of the cruiser as the deputy tucked his flashlight under his arm. Then sort of as an afterthought the rotted tooth, whiskey breathed bully turned back. "Aw man, officer," he said looking at Travis's name tag. "Sergeant Tarvon, how 'bout... ."

Before he even finished the sentence, sans any warning, and before Travis could react, the brawny man was on him. The flashlight fell as he raised his hands to ward off the attack. The assault was so sudden and from such close proximity he didn't have time to move out of the way. Juiced up on drugs and booze some men can act faster than a Texas Bob Cat in heat.

Squeezed into a bear hug Travis knew instantly he was in trouble. Rocking, twisting, kicking, they fell into the ditch next to the roadway, with Travis on the bottom. He immediately felt sharp pain in his rib cage area. They rolled long-ways in the culvert, but Travis was quickly able to pin the man with his left arm while he reached for his portable radio, hoping it would reach from this remote and desolate location.

"FOUR-JOHN-ELEVEN! TEN-SEVENTY-EIGHTY! FOUR-JOHN-ELEVEN," he barked loudly into the mic, trying not to sound panicky.

The dispatcher, in an even and professional voice immediately responded, "4-John-11 . . . 8-William-8."

"8-William-8, in route"

"Okay 8-William-8. 4-John-11."

When he received no response, the seasoned dispatcher continued a monotone monologue with run-together words and sentences that only cops can decipher. "Attention all cars all departments unit 4-John-11 requesting a 10-78 last twenty is farm-to-market four-three-two four miles west of state route eight-twenty-one involves Ford sedan blue in color bearing Texas Tom-Adam-Sam-nine-nine-eight 4-John-11." Travis heard only the heavy breathing and grunts of the man named Hickey.

All across the county every officer with a radio, on-duty or off, began speeding toward the dreaded officer-needs-assistance call. None acknowledged the call or asked permission, fearing that their transmission might override additional information from 4-John-11. One patrolman, in the middle of writing a ticket, suddenly and without a word let the astonished motorist go before racing, code three, to help his brother officer.

Hickey retorted with what could only be described as super human strength. Travis, all two hundred and ten pounds of him, was suddenly thrown across the ditch. Dazed and still trying to get his feet under him, he saw in the strobe light syncopation of the blue flashing emergency lights the foul smelling brute pouncing and screaming, "I'M GOING TO KILL YOU, YOU DIRTY BASTARD!"

Travis had begun to perspire. He hadn't faced his demon in a long time. Maybe he could put it behind him if he looked at it in an objective way. Fat chance. The emotions were and probably would always be too strong. He should have; no, no he wasn't going to play the shoulda, woulda, coulda game tonight. It was pointless. Tonight he would be human, a fallible human being who is not perfect. Tonight he would try to forgive himself. Because if he didn't, how could he expect anyone else to.

As the assailant pounded with his fists, Travis hammered his face with the radio until it shattered. The two men fought for survival in a blackened, muddy ditch lit only by the intermittent flashes of the blue lights. They rolled in the damp muck as Hickey clamped a headlock on the officer with one arm while his free hand ripped Travis's hair. Travis broke the hold when he grabbed Hickey's crotch, squeezing with all his might while biting the heathen's forearm. The taste of blood and sweat fed his animal instincts, intensifying his need to survive.

Suddenly free of each other, Hickey struggled to get up, spewing death threats, while Travis scratched at his holster. To Travis the surrealism of the pseudo time deception phenomenon, tachyinterval, only made the onset of panic more pronounced. He was amazed at how much information his mind could process at a time like this. "Why was it taking so long for his gun to come into battery? Why was his arm taking so long to block the foot that was coming at his head? Where was his back-up? Did the 10-78 call get out? Where were the other occupants of the car?"

The kick, only partially blocked, knocked his service revolver out of his hand and somewhere behind him. The force of Hickey's full leg kick temporarily caused the man to lose his momentum – time for Travis to scramble for the gun. Frantically probing the weeds and debris, he found the weapon and rolled on his side at the instant Hickey leapt on him raining blows to his face. He knew he had to shoot this crazed superman before he lost consciousness, but this scumbag, like he read Travis's mind, grabbed the three-fifty-seven with both hands and turned it toward the Sergeant's face. The two adversaries, now literally nose to nose fought for control. Travis, aware that his finger was exerting pressure on the trigger, maneuvered his left hand to clamp the cylinder and prevent it from being fired. Hickey twisted the magnum into Travis's chest and, still eyeball to eyeball spat, "I'm gonna kill you!" Summoning all his dwindling strength, Travis forced his knees up and with a mighty thrust catapulted gun and man over his head.

Exhausted, arms trembling, Travis clawed at his pants leg and the .38 snub-nose back-up gun strapped to an ankle holster. Eyes riveted on Hickey, highlighted by the eerie glow of the cruiser's taillights, he watched in horror as the big brute leveled the magnum at him. Struggling to bring the small stainless steel revolver into battery Travis heard himself screaming, "NO! NO! NO!"

At less than six feet apart and almost simultaneously, the two weapons spit fire at each other blinding the shooters in brilliant flashes of white hot death. Hickey's first shot tore through Travis's upper leg exiting just below the hip. His second and third shot hit the dirt to the left of the deputy's head. Travis, eyes locked on a shirt chest button, emptied his five shot Chief's Special. Hickey stood stock still.

Completely baffled, Travis thought, "I couldn't have missed him!" The wide-eyed man, the one with the three-fifty-seven, then jumped out of the ditch and ran across the road and into the darkness.

Injured, exhausted and with an empty gun Travis fought to control the onset of panic. Fishing for his pocket knife – his last line of defense – he searched the roadside fearing he'd catch a glimpse of Hickey returning.

Now large numbers of blue flashing lights uniformly lit the area as the back-ups started to arrive. When you're down, out and in need of help, nothing, absolutely nothing, is more comforting, even to a cop, than the presence of a fresh, clean and bright-eyed uniformed officer. Fellow knights in blue with smartly colored arm patches, shiny badges and lots of guns covered the scene. These calm and organized keepers of the peace applied first-aid to Travis, took care of securing the other occupants of the sedan and ordered the ambulance. With flashlights and riot guns at the ready they fanned out and searched for Hickey.

Of Travis's five shots, four struck the intended target. Two of the one-hundred-twenty-five grain semi-jacketed hollow points had ripped the man's heart apart. His body, pumped up on adrenaline and high on alcohol and drugs, had powered him for over a hundred feet into the prairie. He never even knew he was dead.

Travis was drenched in perspiration, his heart beat hard and fast. The dancing lights on his ceiling were gone. He touched the scars on his leg to reassure himself that they were in fact long healed. In the bathroom he rinsed his mouth with Scope to take away the taste of blood and sweat.

He hadn't gone through the whole scenario in a long time – it seemed easier like maybe his mind was also healing. The face that grimaced back at him from the mirror told him that the guilt that had been eating at him all these years was gone. Tonight for the first time he faced the fact that, although he had killed a man, his action was excusable and justifiable. Tonight he could forgive himself and tonight, for the first time, he was certain that God had forgiven him.

BOY GETS GIRL, BOY. . . .

1959/1960 Corvette

As it got closer his suspicions were confirmed - it was a vintage Corvette. Too bad he wasn't driving his old Vette. It could be a fun run over these delightfully twisty and hilly country roads in the outback of the great state of Indiana. Within minutes, on a long straight stretch, the silver, with white inset, fifty-nine/sixty two-seater made its bid to pass.

The familiar rumble of the twin-pipes only made the longing, the recollections, even stronger. What surprised him was that the driver was a lady, a smart looking young lady with long, flame-red hair that trailed out over the rear deck of her open roadster.

Memories of another redhead in a Corvette, back when the Vette was new, quickened his pulse and flooded his mind. She gave a quick look and a smile at midpoint, just as she smacked third gear and dumped a set of quads. And with a chirp of rubber she was gone.

A glance at his speedometer told him that the little excitement had caused him to push his seventy-two El Camino to well above the legal limit. Ah, there was a time when he would have relished a high speed run, but at fifty-three years of age and driving a "stocker," Jack Cambry knew better.

Twenty miles on down the road he still couldn't shake the memory of Natalie. It came back in a rush overwhelming his mind - everything from her in-bred sophistication, to the time in the back seat of her fifty-five Bel-Air; strains of "their song," the Crew Cuts, Angels in the Sky, playing softly over the radio. He hadn't thought of her in a long time and was confused as to why her familiarity - the longing - was so strong. Perhaps it was the guilt that ground the spider gears of his mind.

She had a long pony tail the first time they met. He had just transferred to a new school and she had come over to him during that first recess. He was lonely and scared but she flipped her pony tail and just said, "Hi, I'm Natalie and I hope you like it here," or something to that effect. Her hair was a soothing deep auburn not the fire red of a Rita Hayworth. They were standing under the pavilion watching the sixth graders in a game of kickball.

She was nice and very pretty but he never let on that he thought so...must have been afraid of getting teased or just too young or something. Funny how some recollections are crystal clear and others are hazy.

Their first date hadn't been for four more years until they were sixteen and he had wheels. Now that he thought about it she was his first real date. Oh, he'd met girls at the Saturday matinee and even kissed a few at games of post office or spin the bottle. But Natalie was the first real date. He couldn't remember how they came to go out; maybe it was when a gang of kids were all standing around the soda fountain at Richter's Pharmacy talking about the up-coming sock hop. Yeah, that was it. She said to nobody in particular, but she was looking at him, that she wanted to go but didn't have a ride.

He laughed to himself remembering that first date. Why she ever went out with him again after he made a total fool of himself was a mystery. He had tried to ace some cat in a '52 Olds at a stop light, but stalled by dumping the clutch on an under revved engine. Not very cool on a first date. But, the car was cool, as only a Corvette could be.

> In conversations oblivious to others
> twice his hand she did touch.
> That caused a quickened heart
> which he liked very much.

She was some dish. Not only was she tom-boyish good-looking, but she had a `55 Chev. She had removed the hood and trunk ornaments in preparation for a nose and deck job on this Power-pack stick and had installed spinner hubcaps and a chrome air cleaner herself. She knew more about cars than most guys. She was perfect. Even at sixteen and until they parted at eighteen they fit together, like a valve to a keeper or a connecting rod to a wrist pin.

They had such fun together, he, Natalie and the Vette. They almost never missed a Sunday at the drag strip. He'd be stuck in "B" Sports Car against a lot of usually faster machines and she'd run his Corvette in the Powder Puff class and pull trophy most every time.

How'd it happen? They'd dated - gone steady actually - broken up, then got back together just before his car club's annual dance. Yeah, it was the evening of the Knights' big dance when he got pulled by Herb's '57 Fury that everyone had said was a dog. It was no stocker. To this day he was sure Herb had an Isky Five-Cycle cam and maybe more cubes than came from the factory.

He was angry all evening and when they all stopped at Spooner's drive-in for an after-dance Coke he had tried to put the make on Herb's date. That was also the night Natalie had picked to tell him her Dad had been transferred out of state. He had only meant to get back at Herb for goading him into a race that was a set-up in the first place.

Though they saw each other a few more times before he left for college and she for Chicago, he never really got a chance to apologize or anything. The next year was a little hazy. He had gotten involved with some chick at OSU, rushed a fraternity and flunked out of school. Next thing he knew he was in the Navy.

Wow, the parade of memories from just seeing an old car - an old Corvette - driven by a red headed honey! Oh, he'd thought about her, especially when the loneliness of military life had almost consumed him and again when he committed himself to marriage.

He believed he had really been in love with Sue Ellen, but, Natalie was always somewhere deep in the reserve fuel tank of his mind. When Sue Ellen left him (maybe he never was completely committed to her) he had hunted for Natalie. The search only lasted until he learned she was married.

The yellow diamond shaped sign indicated a right followed by a left, both with a suggested safe speed of forty. He knew he wasn't in a Corvette and he wasn't a teen-ager, but the urge was too great as he set the classic pick-up into the first bend at a little over 70. He rode it through on rails pretending it was a four wheel drift, getting hard on the gas at the apex of each turn. It felt good; engine, speed, noise and...memories.

Daydreaming sure does help while the miles away. Already he was over halfway to Chicago. It had been such a beautiful day that he had driven the old way through the countryside of farm belt America, the route before the Interstate.

Slowing for a small burg he noticed the silver and white Vette parked at the side of a Shell station. Well, he needed gas anyway, and Shell was one of the cards he carried. It sure wouldn't hurt to take a few minutes to look at the vehicle of the past hour's recollections.

A cursory exam of the sports car yielded the knowledge that it was a 1959 model and had a 6500 RPM red line on the tach which indicated it came with a factory 270 or 290 horsepower engine. Absorbed in a world of automobilia he didn't see her until she was standing right next to him.

"Excuse me, sir. I'd like to get into my car."

She couldn't have been much more than twenty-five and could have passed as Natalie's twin if it were thirty plus years ago.

"I'm sorry. I was just admiring your Vette. Had it long?"

"Well, we've owned it for about five years but it was only in the last six months that we've had the time and money to get it into running shape," she said with a smile that showed a slight over bite.

"You are a credit to Corvette owners of old by the way you handled it back there on the open road. Drove like a pro or your daddy owns the road," he joked, trying to expand the moment.

"Wrong on both counts, mister. I'm not a professional and my daddy died last year. So if you'll excuse me...."

"I'm sorry for intruding. It's just that this car stirred thoughts of another Corvette and another red head too many years ago. The car got traded and the red head...I guess she's lost forever."

She reached for the door handle, stopped, turned toward him and said, "No, I'm the one who should be sorry. I'm not in a good mood. I just broke up with my boyfriend. I know you old timers get all twisted out of shape at the sight of machines like this. Uh, the car has the original two-eighty-three engine, bored sixty thousandths over, twin four barrels and an oh-two-seven, solid-lifter, Duntov cam powered through a four-speed transmission and three-seventy rear axle.

"Say, you do know your stuff. Learn it from your dad? He asked, trying not to sound conciliatory.

"I learned mostly from my mom. It's her car and we made a project of rebuilding it. We had the mechanical work done at a shop in Louisville, that's where my mom's from. We did the interior and all the body work ourselves, except the final paint," the red haired beauty stated proudly.

At the mention of Louisville and a widow who knew cars, a chill with the speed of a small-block Chevy, swept over him. An intense smile exposed a face full of age lines as his clear hazel eyes studied her features - red hair, the slightly up-turned nose, the high cheek bones and that slight overbite with very small teeth....

"Why are you looking at me like that? Are you going to hit on me, pal? Come on, let me get into my car I've got places to go," she scolded, brushing past him to vault into the driver's seat.

"I'm, I'm sorry," he stammered. "Was...is you mother's name, Wilson?"

"No, Her name's Minderman. Now please let me go." She twisted the key firing up all eight cylinders with the unmistakably familiar throaty roar of the short-stroke Chevy.

With a rap of the accelerator that sent the little engine revving past three grand she lifted the "T" handle and slapped the lever into reverse. He stepped back, smarting from the false and brash accusation, still overwhelmed by the memories and similarities. He looked at his shoes waiting for her to back away.

The Vette, engine loping at seven-fifty RPM, didn't move. He snuck a glance. Maybe he was still in her way. Boy was he embarrassed. The girl with Rita Hayworth hair and the features of a teenage lost love was staring at him, mouth agape.

Barely audible, over the rumble of the two-seventy, he heard her say, "Yes. You mean my mother's maiden name? Yeah, it was Wilson. Did you know her?" She turned her head as if checking the rear view mirror then turned back again, eyes wide. "Oh wow! If your name's Jack then my mom's been looking for you."

Insignia: Federal Bureau of Investigation

Dateline: Washington

AP International

Data from recently released Pentagon sources reveals that U.S. Army intelligence is investigating a new and significant communication transmitting method. This messaging system is on a heretofore undiscovered frequency, alpha-beta Zertz, or ABZ. It appears that the ability to facilitate messages, subconsciously, on a mass scale has been unprecedented, until now. Preliminary indications of this highly technical matter, under the code name, 2032 Prelude, demonstrated that technology is now available to simultaneously transmit messages directly to any and all humans via, for lack of a better word, mental telepathy. It was not clear if the recipient needed to have a special receiver or any receiver at all.

The information was gleaned from documents included with a Freedom of Information request by this reporter. A full study of these papers was not completed nor is likely at this time. Pentagon officials, claiming the report was released by mistake and not subject to the Freedom of Information Act, physically took back the manuscripts before they could be thoroughly examined.

During a later telephone interview, Army Major Theodore Druffel, spokesman for the Pentagon, told this reporter it was never a project and 2032 Prelude was only a request for funding for a long forgotten and unfunded aspiration of a now defunct domestic intelligence branch of the Army. A White House spokesperson has denied all knowledge of any project using that code name or if such capabilities exist or are even in the planning stages.

A.F. Andrews, Staff Reporter.

FBI Special Agent Carrie Cutter drew the drapes, put on an old Frank Sinatra and lit the center candle of the sterling five-stick candelabra on the Henkel-Harris sideboard. Agent Conner had excused himself to the bathroom where he used his finger to brush his teeth.

Though they had known each other from previous cases, this was the first time they had worked out of the same office and now the flames, like the muzzle flash from their issue side arms, blazed. Almost immediately after stepping into her apartment, they came to each other without reserve. Tenderly he kissed her parted lips just for the sensation and pleasure of teasing. She responded with a soft purring while parting his charcoal and silver mane with long, sharp, crimson fingernails. The candle danced, Frank crooned and the lovers-hopeful swooned. Pressed tightly together as if trying desperately to be one, he loosened her blouse as she pulled his shirt from his pants. The crimson nails, almost the same shade as her hair but not nearly as bright as the fire that burned in her thighs, raked his back. The kiss turned to can't-get-close-enough hugs, the

71

caressing became exploratory as hands and arms roamed from thighs to shoulders.

Taking her face gently in his hands Conner whispered, "Pretty lady. Pretty, pretty Carrie. I wish it could be more."

Turning her head to kiss his hand she said softly, "But?"

He showered her face with kisses. "But, I'm not sure what love is anymore. It's been so long, and the hurt was so deep."

Her answer was to kiss him hard as her hands fumbled with his belt buckle. His manhood stirred and urges surged throughout his body. Gently, he placed his hand on hers and said softly, "Don't. I don't think we should. I want you so bad. It's not right — not yet."

She buried her head in his neck and hugged him with all her might. They held tight until Frank finished 'How little we know'. The lady led the gentle-man to the couch.

"Do you want to tell me about her? I want to hear. I want to know all about you, Seebee . . . and how did you come to that nickname?"

He snuggled her to his side and spun his mind back to another life. "Other than the Seebee standing for my initials, C, B, it goes back to grade school when I used to answer 'could be' to any challenge such as kids saying things like, do you wana make somethin' out of it or do ya wanna fight?

As to my wife, I met her, fell in love, or what I thought at the time was love, got married and got divorced. So what's to tell?"

"I'm sorry. If it's too painful, maybe some other time," she said, laying her hand on his leg, careful to place it closer to his knee than his thigh.

"No. I'm the one who's sorry. Maybe it's not as bad as I think it was. Time has a way of healing all. It was only recently that I was finally able to put to rest another painful and traumatic event."

He settled into the couch, relaxed and looked at her face to read the reaction to his next admission. "I had to kill a man once."

For the first time the muzzle flashes were only bright flames of light. He was a different person then — in a different life. That realization, that understanding, overwhelmed him and he began to choke up, tears forming and rolling down his cheeks obliterating his vision.

"Oh, I'm sorry, Seebee, I didn't mean to...."

"It's okay." He pressed her head back into his chest, kissing the top of her head. "I'm free. I'm crying because for the first time I know. I know that I'm not to blame for everything." He told her about the dirtbad he had to engage in a firefight and of how he had felt guilt for so long — of how he met the demon in his mind and put it to rest. And now he could, and did, finally forgive himself.

"What about the woman? Do you need forgiveness?"

"I guess I do. I promised to make her dreams come true. I never knew what her dreams were until it was too late. I was young, cocky and a typical chauvinistic cop. I just assumed; I believed that her dreams were the same as mine. I don't know if we ever really compared dreams. Probably we did, but I wasn't listening. I didn't know how to listen. When she told me she was leaving me; and as much as I hurt inside, I couldn't, wouldn't even talk about what she felt or wanted. I just kept saying how much I loved her and that she had a duty, like she was some kind of sworn fellow police officer, to stay with me. Boy, was I a controlling, pompous jerk. She probably hurt as much as I did."

Sitting straighter and trying not to be so melodramatic he continued, "That was the old Conner Baakeman who bears no resemblance to the fine, upstanding new Conner Baakeman now sitting before you." He grinned and winked.

"What happened to her?"

"She moved in with her folks near Chicago, became a very successful stock broker and married a man five years her junior. I still get a birthday card from her every year and we've remained on good terms."

"Did you have any kids?"

"Nope. Our dream, I thought it was hers too, was to wait until we had a larger nest egg. Anyway, now you know my whole life story. It could have been worse. Okay...your turn."

"I think we're good for each other. After law school, I worked for a time at a law firm, but I couldn't wrap my mind around trying to defend some Toop and I didn't want to be a street cop, thus the Bureau took me under their wing. I too, faced my past and granted myself absolution. Though I never killed anyone, I believed I was responsible for the death of my son for a very long time."

He held her tight, occasionally kissing the top of her head as she honored the memory of her only child.

"What's a Toop?"

"Tee, double oh, pea, is what we called the dirtbags the court assigned us to defend. We weren't allowed to call them scumbags or other terms of endearment so we referred to these recidivistic losers as Temporarily Out Of Prison, TOOPs."

Half laying arm in arm, the talk turned to caresses and then kisses. With the fires again burning strongly he cupped a breast in his calloused hand, whispering, "We could be a whole lot more comfortable if we were between blue things."

"Blue things? What blue things?"

"Those nice soft pretty blue sheets on...."

"On my bed! How do you know what color my sheets are?" Carrie asked, incredulously.

"I peeked when I went up to the bathroom. Don't look at me like that. A good agent always checks things out."

"What else did you...investigate? Wait a minute. A little while ago you said you didn't think it would be the right thing to do?"

"I lied."

"Well then," Carrie snuggled closer. "Why don't I go upstairs, slip into my black lace peek-a-boo teddy, climb between those crisp and fresh 'blue things' while you...GO HOME — you teaser!"

He laughed and squeezed her tight. "You know, we're good for each other."

The following morning each, separately and about ten minutes apart, entered their office building and walked under a large welcome sign that had been recently installed by the landlord of this seven story building. The building housed government as well as commercial tenants. Upon passing through their security checkpoint, Senior Special Agent Wyler, pulled, first Seebee and then, when she checked in, Agent Cutter into the clean room.

Even before being seated, Wyler began, "The 2032 Prelude we all learned about, thanks to an AP reporter, could be real. I have notified the Director and he has ordered a team of agents to pick up the reporter. The proof of the reality was discovered right here in this building.

"One of the building's security agents observed very strange behavior on the atrium floor yesterday morning and brought the tape from the video monitor to me. He is under my personal direction not to divulge what he saw. The tape showed everyone, during a two hour period, who passed under the welcome sign to have raised their hand. I repeat, everyone. Let me show you what the camera caught."

Fifty-seven year old Tom Wyler had been in law enforcement from before he was born – his mother was a Juvenile Officer for Lupine County S.O. and his father, until he was gunned down, was a Detective Lieutenant in and for the same county. Tom's first LE position was with Dade County Metro where he worked as a patrol officer until being accepted by the Bureau. He never married.

As the video ran, Wyer noted again, how everyone raised his or her hand, but Agent Cutter noticed something else. "If you look closely, it appears all the men are raising their right hand while the women are raising their left hand. I say appears, because one women is raising her right hand."

"Perhaps a glitch or the women raising her right hand is in fact a man in drag," Wyler said. "The security officer and I identified and interviewed many of the people on the video. What is really significant about this unprecedented behavior is that none of them remember either raising their hand or noticing others had raised a hand or even being told to raise their hand. In addition, none of the twelve cameras in different parts of the building detected similar behavior. To put it another way, this power to command action and erase all memory of this action might not only be gender selective, but also location specific."

Seebee said, "It's not an insurmountable problem. We just have to find who has this power and make sure it's not used against our -

America's - best interest. Of course, at best, best is an ambiguous term and. . . ."

Wyler interrupted, "It doesn't say the Army created a new method – just that they are investigating a communication band, something Zertz, whatever that means. The seriousness of this is that it appears to have already been tested, if that is the right word, on people. I would doubt, in this day and age of liability issues, our military would be practicing on unsuspecting American citizens. That leaves foreign nations, other highly sophisticated organizations or even something that has invaded our universe. . . ."

Wyler paused, looked the other agents in the eye and then continued. "A short time ago, I was privy to attend a special conference with the President, our Director and two well-known theologians. The purpose of this very esoteric meeting was to postulate reasons why we, the Judeo-Christian world, are at such odds with the Muslim world. The gist of this meeting included the religious representative's view that there is more than one god."This is the way it was explained: Somewhat over 3000 years ago, God delivered the Ten Commandments to Moses. One of those commandments said, depending on which version of the Bible you read, words to the effect: You shall not recognize the gods of others.

"In other words, God is acknowledging there are other gods. Conventional thinking has always been; other gods means idols, statutes and related physical property. Perhaps not. Consider the possibility that other gods might mean the gods of different peoples, such as the Asians, Indians, Arabs, Africans, et al.

"These other peoples could have been fashioned in the image of their god.

"Supplementary evidence comes when God tells Moses to command Joshua to enter Canaan and kill all the Canaanites. Canaan is, of course, also known as The Land of Milk & Honey, or a.k.a. modern day Israel. If our God was the god of all peoples, why would He order the slaughter of His own making? He wouldn't. Maybe, He is ordering the killing of another god's "people." Conceivably, our God and the god of other peoples are in competition – at war – with each other and we could merely be pawns in their game of trying to best the other."

"So, what you're saying is, some supreme authority is using unknown powers to tell us what to do?" Seebee said.

"Yes, that's a possibility?"

"Okay, I can buy that. However, also consider that it might be a god or supremacy – call it what you will- from another universe? It's always been said; 'God works in mysterious ways'." Carrie replied.

Seebee said, "Perhaps, it could be said; 'the devil also works in mysterious ways?' This might not be serious if, say a retail business could make customers buy certain products or if the military could force their battle field opponents to lay down their weapons. That is, if we are the controllers. I think the best course of action for us, as a group, is to immediately seek an audience with the President to exhibit the surveillance tapes."

FBI Special Agents Cutter, Baakeman and Wyler, each armed with the standard issue .40 caliber Glock pistol, stood in unison and began walking toward the door. All three knew going outside the chain of command was verboten. But, that ingrained thought never crossed their minds. Walking under the Welcome sign in the atrium, Wyler and Seebee raised their right hand while Carrie raised her left hand.

STILL A SECRET

4-6-4 Steam Locomotive

The piercing light was visible long before he heard the two longs followed by two shorts as the Chicago bound James Whitcome Riley approached the Carter Street crossing. Within minutes the E-9, the most powerful of diesel engines, was thundering into Winton Place station. Though the little two piece windshield, just aft of the giant single head lamp, towered over his head he couldn't suppress the smile and memory of last week's Christmas. Then it was he who towered over an E-9, a Lionel with "Santa Fe" splashed in orange and silver across the side of his gift to a wide-eyed nephew.

From his vantage point, near the Western Union window, Kurt Kidwell could see the platform to the right and the parking lot to his left. The target was nowhere to be found. Maybe Miss Dolly had set him up - they were traveling by car and it was a bum steer. He watched, ticket in hand, as the porters loaded and unloaded boxes, grips, trunks and all sizes of suitcases. He scrutinized the passengers as they embarked and disembarked, especially the smart looking tan-suited knockout with the matching hat perched atop her stacked honey blond hair. Kidwell never took his eye off the lot. Maybe he was already on-board having caught the train at the Oakley Station?

The man who earned a living watching, watched, with a sinking feeling, as the Brakeman, lantern in hand, got into position at the rear of the train. It had begun to rain. Kidwell stepped toward the Pullman car, Starlight, as the sound of tires straining for adhesion on gravel commanded his attention. Caught in the head lamps of a dirty black '49 Cadillac convertible, the trademark of Mr. Pogue, Kidwell pulled the brim of his fedora a little lower and the collar of his trench coat up as he stepped onto the Starlight's platform.

The Brakeman began to move his lantern up and down, the signal for the engineer to get underway. Mr. Pogue and his driver, laden with two suitcases and a string tied cardboard box, had to be helped by the Brakeman onto the now moving train.

He'd give Pogue an hour or so then he'd look him up. He wasn't going anywhere for at least a few hours - the Riley's first stop. Right now Kidwell needed the men's room and some warm food. Entering the day-coach, El Capitan, he searched the overhead racks for a place to stash his hat and coat. Amid leather suitcases, paperboard composite grips and round lady's' hat boxes with the name of swank department stores emblazoned on the richly colored Krome-kote wrapping, he found an unobtrusive spot. The car's seats were filled more with small trunks, a few leather trimmed canvas covered grips and gift boxes than the holiday travelers themselves. Tossed on and between were an array of coats and outer wear, a leather flyer's jacket, a smartly creased gentleman's felt hat with a tweed sport jacket and a hangered sailor's dress blues. The lavatory was clean, properly stocked and a great relief.

The dining car was about half full so Kidwell had no trouble settling into a starched linen covered table, complimented with a small bouquet of fresh flowers snugged up to the window. Within a minute the hospital-white clad waiter filled Kidwell's order for a Jack Daniels on the rocks. Complacency settled over the Private Investigator as he casually observed soothed couples' happy faces reflected by the individual table lamps against their personal half-shaded windows. Entrées enjoyed were a choice of Prime Rib, Boursin Chicken or Stuffed Lemon Sole as America's backyards roll by. The dressed to the nines, tan-suited knockout smiled at him over the top of a tall cold exotic something. Kurt Kidwell discreetly adjusted his shoulder holster before approaching tan-suit.

"I'm Karl Kinder, may I join you?" he asked, athletically jostling his muscular body into the opposite seat as the train rocked over a set of switches. The pseudo name was one he used when dealing with strangers while on the job. In this business, you never know who's also on the job on the opposite side.

"Seems that you already have, and I'm happy to meet you, I think. My name is Victoria and that, that drunken soldier who just came in has been bothering me. Uh, oh, here he comes again."

"Well . . . there you are little lady. I thought I lost ya. Is thesh man bothering you," the three-stripe non-com slurred.

"I think it's the other way around, Sergeant. The lady is with me so please refrain from interfering with us again," Kurt said, in a kind manner, rising from his seat while boring his eyes into a set of slightly dilated pupils.

It was really all one move, the words, the stare and the arm lock that crumpled the uniform to his knees. Reducing the pressure enough to allow the intruder to be half dragged, Kidwell deposited the rude soldier in the forward sleeper admonishing him to sleep it off.

Returning to his upholstered dinner table chair beneath the car length, hand-painted murals covering the frieze on both sides of the pre-war dining car, the lady named Victoria smiled again, "Thank you ever so much, Mr. Kinder." The soft pastel colors highlighted by the hanging globe lights lent an aura of mystic and intrigue to this calm and sophisticated lady.

During the interlude that preceded the main course the widowed heir to an old manufacturing company and the gentleman with the clandestine demeanor, carefully exchanged pleasantries.

They dined on filet mignon with sautéed mushrooms and fresh spinach au gratin. When the plates had been cleared they sipped Three Star Hennessey as winking roadside crossings lights occasionally flashed across the darkened window. He told her his business was corporate acquisitions and he, also, was on his way home to Chicago.

The train, now at cruising speeds of seventy plus, set up a gentle rocking motion which, between cars as he was seeing her to her bedroom compartment, caused her to fall into him. He steadied her, feeling firm upper arms and catching a scent of Channel Number Five. They stood close to let another passenger pass. The vibes oozed. "I've got some business to take care of," he said, locking into her light green eyes. "If I stop back in an hour or so can we have a night cap?"

She returned his gaze before twisting, brushing against his arm, as she unlocked the door, "I'd like that. I need to freshen up a little, anyway."

Since Pogue hadn't visited the dining car he had to be between there and the club car. Kidwell set out to scout the train. The top half to the outside door of the car just ahead of the lounge car was open, a fact noted by the PI in case anything had to be tossed out. Stepping into the club car, the classic model with a half length mahogany bar down one side, Kidwell smiled to the lone bartender as his eyes scanned the room. Seated in the fore section was a businessman studying a newspaper next to his young, comic book reading son and next to the boy a fidgeting, beer drinking sailor. Halfway back, Mr. Pogue, holding the twine tied box, and his chauffeur were complacently sipping drinks. Kidwell walked the length of the room and sat at the rear most table - after surreptitiously verifying the door to the observation platform was unlocked. The bartender looked up, but the private dick shook his head while picking up a Life magazine.

He didn't like the situation. He didn't like all the witnesses. He didn't like the driver, if that's what he really was. If he was a driver, then why did he leave the Caddy at the train station and why did he keep looking around - like a body guard.

The diesel horn sounded, two longs followed by two shorts for the approach of a public crossing. The now tense six foot P.I. had been counting since the first. The engineer had been very punctual. Almost exactly eleven seconds after the first blast of the horn the sound of the crossing bells reached the train's passenger cars. The bells, combined with the flashing red lights bouncing through the train's windows, were quite distracting.

The sailor got up to leave, the P.I. started another magazine. It didn't look like Pogue was in any hurry by the number of olive pits in the ash tray. Body guard was sipping something dark with ice through a straw - probably a Coke if he was on the job. Kidwell had hoped to have concluded the business by now, but there had been too many people and he hadn't counted on a body guard.

The mission had seemed simple enough when the phone call came, followed by the packet of cash and directives. All he had to do was trade the package Mr. Pogue was to be transporting for the cash Kurt was carrying in his inside jacket pocket. He was instructed to secure the package at all costs, something about a threat to national security. It seemed his clientele only called when the task was too tough or sticky for lesser agents.

When the executive and his son rose to leave, Kurt signaled the bartender. He asked the practiced elderly Negro if he would be so kind as to check with the kitchen for an order of cheese and crackers. Now there were only three.

"Mr. Pogue, I'd like a word... ."

"Mr. Pogue don't talk to nobody, so take a powder, pal," the burly body guard belched forcing his way between them.

Time was short before the barkeep or another passenger would walk in. Kidwell lowered his eyes and turned slightly to send body language messages of capitulation while he searched for words to stall for time and a piece of luck. Softly he began, "I'm sorry sir, I didn't mean to intrude it's only that . . . the words were lost to the wail of the E-9's horn . . . won't bother . . . eight - nine - ten - the bells clanged, the lights flashed, the bruiser's concentration broke as he glanced out the windows. Just like the sergeant, and so many others before him, it was all one move. The P.I.'s foot found the male tender spot just below the belly button an instant before the palm of the right hand connected just under the jaw of the stunned and buckling galoot.

Mr. Pogue, impaired by the martinis, could only stare, slack jawed, as Kurt dragged the unconscious body through the rear doors and onto the observation platform. The thought of tossing the dead weight over was tempting, but he had confidence that his body guarding days were over for the night.

"Now then Mr. Pogue, before we were so rudely interrupted, we have business to transact. I have here," Kidwell began extracting the envelope filled with cash from his jacket pocket, "A large sum of money that I intend to trade you for the box on your lap."

"What have you done with Bruno. It's not for sale, now please leave me or I shall summon the authorities. Bartender, bartender... ."

"I sent him away. It's just you and me. Time is short and you only have two choices."

"What do you mean? Who are you? I'm not selling. All you and your kind want to do is keep it off the market. My invention will... ."

As the inventor rambled on, Kidwell took the man's half drained highball from the table top and casually tossed it into his face. The slightly intoxicated keeper of the box reacted before he realized he had relaxed his grip on the box. That was all the practiced P.I. needed. He flipped the envelope on the table and strode out, catching out of the corner of his eye, the opening platform door and the guard struggling in, revolver in hand!

"Is it a present for me?" the golden haired lady impishly chided as she opened the door at his knock. "Or is it a reward from rescuing other maidens?"

His face relaxed and a smile spread to his dimples as he surveyed the room and the silk robe clad lady. But his mind was racing. "Sorry to put you to any trouble, but I'm in a bit of a jam and I might need your help."

He put the box down on the day couch, turned to look her in the eye to see if she was with him. She held her head high and stared back at him. He took her squared shoulders in his powerful hands pulling her toward him. It was a closed mouth kiss, he afraid of relaxing, and she, just to let him know the quid pro quo was sealed.

He told her the box contained medical experiments that a Russian agent, an armed Russian agent on board the train, was trying to steal from him. "Look, I think the train is going to stop soon and when it does I'll need you to get off with me. They won't be looking for a couple, especially one with glasses," he said producing a pair of eye glasses with clear lenses.

It didn't take long before the sound of the thug could be heard in the passage way, banging on every door. There wasn't time to discuss anything.

Bang, bang, bang, "Open the door."

Slowly she opened the door a crack. The bully, gun in hand, pushed, slamming it against the closet. "What's the meaning of this… ."

"Shut up. Where is he?"

"How dare you. There's no one in here. Who… ." He pushed passed her, looking first toward the beds then at the water closet door.

Kidwell, back to the wall, crouched in the tiny, crowded, pitch-black toilet room. He eased his HSc Mauser out of its shoulder holster and leveled it at the door. Even over the click-clack of the train's wheels he could hear the distinct click of the door handle as the Mauser's safety clicked off.

Having killed before and in control of the situation, fear was absent, though he was, maybe a mite apprehensive. The little 7.65 pocket pistol, taken from a Nazi officer he had garroted during his days in the service of his country, was a favorite of his arsenal of concealable weapons. Its reliability had been established in past operations.

BlaaaaaaaaaaaaCrack,Crack,Crackaaaaaaaat. The timing of the diesel locomotion's announcement that it was approaching a station couldn't have been more opportune.

The aggressor, dumbfounded at the three thirty-two caliber crimson holes in his shirt front, paradoxically glimpsed the lavatory mirror for his final vision - the face of a dead man.

"Victoria, Victoria give me a hand, he's fallen on me."

The previously formal and composed lady Victoria, ashen and wide eyed, nonetheless dutifully straddled the body and extended a hand.

84

"Get dressed and put on some lipstick, we're getting off here." She stood there, gaping at the corpse as the impact of the situation began to sink in. Struggling with her suit case, he slapped her hard on the rump. "Get moving, NOW!"

With the smaller of her two suitcases he dumped their contents on the bed, placed the string tied box inside, and packed what he could of the dumped contents around the box.

"What we can't get into your other suitcase, I'll replace," he stated, throwing undergarments and personal items into the larger grip as the train slowed for the station stop.

Victoria, displaying genuine aristocratic style, smiled as she accompanied the P.I. through the El Capitan where he retrieved his hat and coat. As a cold wind whipped at their ankles they snuck across the platform to a waiting cab.

The hotel in this out-of-the-way little burg was, if nothing else, a safe haven. Here, as the lady bathed, he inspected the contents of the box he had killed for.

After his shower, and standing in his under shorts, he moved to take her into his arms, "I just want to hold you."

"You mean gratuitously? For helping you conduct whatever dirty business you're in? Perhaps you better tell me who you really are, Mr. Karl Kinder, if that's your real name." She had regained her full stature as a business executive. "You have presented yourself as a gentleman, at least in your dealings with me. Please continue to do so. I have no intention of allowing this room to become a tryst."

"I understand and respect your wishes. All I said was I wanted to hold you. I need a little tenderness now and I thought you might also."

"Who are you? What... ."

"It's best that you don't know my real name. I'm a private investigator and sometimes my assignments get a little ah . . . hairy. I'm sorry to have involved you in this, but making use of you as cover seemed like a good idea at the time. After this matter is concluded I'd like to try to start all over - on a social level, especially since we're both from Chicago. Right now, I think we each could use a little, make that a lot, of TLC."

She came to him. They hugged. The tension dissipated. In a short while they fell asleep.

Hours later he slipped out, paid the hotel bill and, box in hand, wolfed down a pancake breakfast at a greasy spoon two blocks down the street. Finding himself in the seedier part of town he quickly located a pawn shop where he purchased a used canvas suitcase in which to carry the box.

He caught a cab to the station, bought a ticket on the next train to Chicago and found a public telephone. Three rings and he heard his client, "Consolidated Gas and Oil, Incorporated, may I help you?" the sweet voice of a young operator answered.

"Extension 4-4-7, Please"

"Yes."

"This is Kidwell."

"Have you got it?"

"Yes sir."

"Where are you? Tell me what's in the box."

"I'm a couple of hours out of the LaSalle Street Station. The box contains a lot of diagrams, blue prints and legal papers plus what looks like a carburetor - a special kind of carburetor."

"Excellent. Come directly to the Drake. We will meet you in the lobby."

He had a half hour to kill before departure. Maybe he could find a little something for Miss Dolly. She had really come through for him, but the thought of a special lady is what was really twisting around in his mind. He took a walk around the block, past a Negro bar where he stopped to listen to a solo coronet crying some blues number that drifted by like a spirit on the winds of time.

Author's note: Rumors have circulated since the 1930s that a man named Pogue (or Fish or ???) invented a carburetor that produced unprecedented fuel economy. The rumor includes the scenarios that the petroleum producers, foreign interests and/or the automobile manufacturers, to keep the product off the market, stole the design and to keep Mr. Pogue/Fish/??? quiet, paid him off or. . . .

II Non-Fiction Stories

Early Hot Rod Sedan

Atop the control tower

at any drag race

runs the announcer's mouth

at a constant and fever pace

"First off we have a few announcements. The ice man hasn't made the scene yet so if you're in need of a cold Coke or somethin' you're gonna have to wait. He is expected within the hour. Next all you cats who plan on racing today please use gate "B" as in baby, baby, baby."

HOT ROD: n. Performance enhancing a factory vehicle to increase its horsepower, acceleration and speed.

Though hot rodding began in the 1930s the effects of the Great Depression and World War II greatly suppressed its numbers. The glory years really didn't get started until the 1950s and carried on into the early sixties. Hot rodding, especially street racing, became more prevalent due to an improved economy that had hindered the cash-strapped/gasoline-rationed past generation. Sans sanctioned drag strips, racing on the streets and highways were the only option for this new generation of pioneer hot rodders.

In addition, lagging police technology fueled this open road mentality that made "getting caught" a remote probability. More powerful Detroit-built cars were often the result of hot rodder innovations such as multiple carburetors, hi-performance cams and machining techniques that pushed the limits of factory production. Most of these mechanical changes were discovered by trial and error, but when they worked the "Big Three" (Ford, Chrysler, GM) took notice. Many of these "trials" significanty improved performances. "Errors" occurred when, say for example, one hot rodder learned that someone had successfully shaved .100 in. off his flywheel to which this hot rodder would think: if .100 in. is good for more speed, then .125 in. would be better. Sometimes these innovations worked and sometimes they caused the modified part to come apart at high speed. Additionally, hopping-up an engine put increased strains on other parts of the car - strains not envisioned or engineered for by the factory.

> *Pony tails and fender skirts and*
> *BABY LET THE GOOD TIMES ROLL.*
> *Ricky Nelson and Jackie Wilson, Little Richard and Jerry Lee,*
> *Hootenannies and SHORT FAT FANNIE*
> *and OH, OH TRAGEDY.*

Drag racing, at first, was a hobby whereas the hot rodder needed his rod for everyday transportation and thus couldn't have a "full-race" engine or a show-quality finish. Fact was these modified and customized vehicles were usually never completely finished. Most exhibited primer paint and lacked upgraded interiors and spit-shined/chrome-plated engines - in direct contrast to hot rods of today. This was mostly due, not so much because the rodder didn't have the time or money to complete the car, but usually as a result of taking on a new responsibility...such as marriage and all that comes with.

In the Glory Years, drag strips were little in number and fought against by local politicians. However, once city fathers were convinced that hot rod clubs were serious about legal racing and would punish club members who were caught racing on the streets, drag strips became more prevalent. In most communities, hot rod clubs would ban together to form an association and then seek a sympathetic police officer to help convince the political powers to authorize the building of a drag strip.

The "Big Three," learning from the hot rodders innovations and demands for more horsepower, began offering factory options such as hot cams, multi-carb set-ups and engineered drive trains to handle this increase in engine power. By the mid-sixties hot-rodding, as the innovators had lived it, was passé. No longer was it possible to win a race just because you could hop-up or do a better tune-up than the other guy. The advent of the "muscle car" era marked the beginning of the, who-ever-has-the-most-money wins the race. Sanctioned, produced and funded factory vehicles made drag racing an expensive and technologically intense venture.

Another factor, police technology, also contributed to fewer street races. At the same time that political subdivisions were considering allowing sanctioned drag strips, they were equipping their police departments with "interceptor" scout cars. These interceptors were mostly just unmarked, V8 powered sedans with heavy duty brakes and dash or grill mounted red-lights. In addition, better radio communication and radar improvements also put a serious damper on those who did their racing on the street.

By the 1980s many former hot-rodders were settled in their careers, had a spare garage bay and began building modern street rods, drag-racing-only vehicles and show-only customs. Though these "finished" cars are what the owner had dreamed of in his early years, it wasn't the same. Then, as today, most all innovations had been discovered and with a spare garage and money one can buy most any part or pay someone

> *to make his wish come true.*
> *Three deuces on an open roaster*
> *Puppy love with a pony tail*
> *Eye tearing wind at a hundred per*
> *The summer of '57 - all hail*

90

With the opening of the Beechmont Drag Strip in Cincinnati, in late 1957, Legal drag racing finally came of age in the Midwest. I was most fortunate to have been there. It all came about with one memorable meeting between S.O.T.A and a city police officer. It was believed mandatory to have the blessing of law enforcement and we, the local hot rodders who made up the Southern Ohio Timing Association, found a friend in motorcycle officer, Carl Poppe. After listening to our pleas and promises to curtail street racing, he agreed to represent us to the city council. It was a revelation. Though only 15 at the time, I was a junior member of The Knights of the 20th Century - one of the hot rod clubs that made up the timing association.

The financing was done with the sale of bonds. However, we only raised enough money to pave the quarter mile thus the shut-down lanes were gravel and the return track was dirt. By opening day, late in the summer of 1957, we had had the return strip coated with copious amounts of used motor oil to keep the dust under control.

Early on it was Elvis and Smokey
the Everly's, Richie and Fats.
Four-on-the-floor or three-on-the-tree
and DARLING COME SOFTLY TO ME.

The spectator and pit areas were grass beaten into dirt which yielded great clouds of dust whenever the wind blew. But nobody really cared - we saw our hard work rewarded when we, at long last, reached the starting line. Club members who weren't racing, either because they didn't have their rod ready, or because, like me, weren't old enough for a license, were still expected to work at the various posts. Not having a license didn't prevent my driving on the strip, because when an errand needed to be run from one end of the strip to the other, I was the first to volunteer to drive S.O.T.A.'s '52 Ford pick-up. I couldn't go over 10 MPH on the return lane for safety reasons, but on the strip I floored the old truck to reach the wild speed of at least 50 MPH!

In those early days my stature among schoolmates was greatly enhanced as I was acknowledged by some of the upper classmen, who had come to race their daddy's car. They'd just say, "Like how's it goin' Chuck?" as I painted the number and class on their window with Bon-ami shoe polish. It was really neat. Here I was, a fifteen-year-old with an official S.O.T.A . armband, a Knights T-shirt and rubbing shoulders with the gods of the local car world. It never occurred to me that perhaps it was these older classmates' stature that was increased; to them, maybe I was one of the gods. This lofty position was responsible for an introduction to Kathy, my first real true love.

She was in the spectator section with a friend of a friend who introduced us. Actually, he was in last year's English class. He called to me as I was performing the task of patrolling the bystander barricade. I stopped and went over to where he and two girls were standing. I don't remember much of what was said after hearing the name Kathy. She was beautiful.

I'm not sure what came out of my mouth other than I had to finish walking the fence line to keep the fans from climbing on it, but she asked if she could walk with me. The race day was almost over, so we didn't get much of a chance to know each other while I completed my task. Mostly, we talked about what music we liked; yes, I liked Elvis, but thought Little Richard was the most. Kathy loved Elvis and Buddy Holly. We both agreed that Buddy Knox's rendition of "Party Doll" was better than Steve Lawrence's and anybody who didn't like Fats Domino was gone. Somewhere, man, a merry-go-round was spinning . . . and I was on it. I was cool enough to get her phone number, which she had to write on a dollar bill because neither one of us had any paper. Using lipstick she wrote her name on one side and her number on the other.

> *Yeah, we were there in the beginning,*
>
> *singing, dancing and spinning,*
>
> *driving, racing and winning.*

I caught a ride home with Benny in his '57, fuel-injected Chevy convertible and told him about the neat chick I'd met and how a girl who liked drag racing and rock & roll music was the one for me. His only comment was "The higher you go the harder you fall," while Sonny James', "Young Love," blared over the speakers in the dash. I wondered what he meant.

When I got home that night Mom was worried because I had missed dinner. In fact, I had missed breakfast and lunch and had eaten only a couple of hot dogs at the strip. I was starved. I sat down in the big kitchen at the counter and without sounding too demanding asked my sister, Bobbi, if she would fix me something. Bobbi said, "Mother, look at him! He's a walking pig pen. I don't even want to be in the same room with him."

"Chuck go up and take a shower and put on some clean clothes, and we'll fix you something to eat," Mom sighed.

Dinner was warmed over pot roast and noodles which was very good; anything would have been good, as hungry as I was. While I ate I tried to tell Mom and Bobbi about my day. They listened without comment until I mentioned that I had met a good looking chick.

"What's her name," asked Bobbi.

"I'm not tellin', so don't bug me," I said, stonewalling.

"She must be some hot rod girl who wears short-shorts. Are you ashamed of her? Why won't you tell us her name?"

"I'll bet you'd wear short-shorts too if you didn't have such a big rear end," I shot back.

"Mother, tell him not to talk to me like that."

"Charles!" Mom said.

"Well then tell her not to bug me about my friends," I replied.

"Next thing you know you'll be growing duck tails and become a bigger hood than you already are," Bobbi said, not missing a chance to slip one in on me.

"I doubt that, man, but at least I don't bleach my hair."

"That's enough children," was Mom's final word.

I was beat, but I just had to call the number on the dollar bill before going to bed. I dialed, trying to imagine what kind of house she lived in, what she was doing now and if she would even remember me. What if she didn't?

"Is Kathy there?"

"Just a moment please."

"Hello." I recognized the voice; it was musical.

"Kathy? Hi, it's Chuck, Chuck Klein; you know, we met at the strip today."

"Oh, hi Chuck." Then a little softer, "I was hoping you'd call."

"Yeah, I thought I'd call before I hit the hay. I'm really beat. It was a long day. I got to the strip about 7:30 this morning and just got home a little while ago."

"You must be awful tired."

"I am. Do you go to the strip often or was this your first time?"

"It was my first time. I only went because my girl friend, Donna, that's the girl I was with, dragged me along because she had a date with Joey and she didn't want to be alone with him,"

"Joey, you mean the cat I saw you with?" I asked.

"Yes, he said he knows you from school."

"I think he was in a class with me last year."

"At Woodward?"

"Yeah, where do you go to school?"

94

"I go to Walnut Hills."

"That's where my sister went; I know a few cats that go there. Do you know Mike Kahn or Ed Goldman?"

"I know who they are," Kathy replied.

"Why didn't your friend want to be alone with Joey?" I asked.

"She only went out with him as a friend. She's trying to break up with him. What's your sister's name? Was she in a sorority?"

"Yeah, she was in STP, but she graduated a year ago. Her name's Bobbi."

"I don't think I knew her. Did you hear the song, "Whole Lotta Shakin' Goin' On," by Jerry Lee Lewis?" Kathy asked.

"Cool man, you can really dance to that one. Do you collect records?"

"No. Do you?"

"No. I've got to put money into my car."

"I have to go now I hear my mom calling to get off the phone. It was nice talking to you, Chuck."

"Yeah, I've got to get to bed. If you're not doing anything next Saturday night, I'd like to see you. Maybe we could double with somebody to the drive-in or something," I suggested, holding my breath for the answer to whether I lived or died.

"That might be okay. Will you call me during the week?" She said, in an up-beat tone.

We said our good-byes, but I could have talked forever. I felt I had known her a long time with what I had already learned. She was about five-feet-three, much shorter than me, had light brown hair that she wore in a ponytail. I wasn't sure about the color of her eyes. I'd better check that next time, first thing, in case she asks if I know. It was time to shag ass and get some z's.

By the mid 60s, the Beechmont Drag Strip, stripped of profitable income, had run its last run. But to those who had been there from the beginning the memories are still burning in the combustion chamber of our minds.

Listed below are some of the vehicles owned by members of the Knights of the 20th Century Hot Rod Club (Cincinnati, Ohio, circa 1957). These unrestored, used cars in most cases were daily drivers and in various stages of completion. With maybe a few exceptions, none were ever "completed".

Studebaker powered '36 Ford;

Cadillac powered '54 Studebaker (Stude-a-lac);

Cadillac powered '50 Mercury (Merc-a-lac)

Full race '52 Olds (the one who's flywheel disintegrated because he removed too much metal);

Flat-head Mercury powered '49 Ford (the one that never made it to the end of the drag strip);

V8 Chev powered '39 Ford;

Chrysler powered '57 Chev;

Chrysler powered '40 Ford;

Olds powered '40 Ford Pick-up

Partly customized '53 Plymouth;

Unfinished, radically customized '56 Chev;

H-modified, Fiberglas bodied, sports car;

One "B" Dragster and a number of 55-57 Chevies and Fords.

LIFE AT THE STRIP

'59 Corvettes being 'flagged' off the line by author, 1960

Deep in the little boy
of all men fully grown,
lives the excitement for a
race engine's pure tone.

It was a beautiful late summer, Sunday morning. A few towering, bulbous, ermine white clouds and a morning temp of about 75 greeted me when I arrived to pick up, Laine, my steady girl.

Her daddy, standing on the porch, looked on, dubiously, as she stepped over the side of my Almquist bodied sports car and settled into the homemade bucket seat. I smiled and waved to him; voice communication being impossible over the noise blasting out of the 750 cubed, straight-piped engine (that's 750 cubic centimeters – not inches). It was well before 8:00 a.m. and I'm sure we woke many of his neighbors in this tree-shaded Cincinnati suburb.

Being a member of S.O.T.A., I need to arrive early at the Beechmont Drag Strip as I would be working with my fellow members of the Knights of the 20th Century hot rod club. We and other Cincinnati area club members formed the Southern Ohio Timing Association that owned the recently N.H.R.A. sanctioned strip. The summer of 1958 was our first full year of operation and today was the regional meet – which meant the trophies would be larger and engraved.

> *I was on my way to the Hop,*
>
> *When I squealed to a stop*
>
> *at the light*
>
> *Ah, ready for a fight. . .*

The sports car started out as a 15th birthday present from my father in the form of a 1952 Crosley two door sedan with its tiny four cylinder engine that barely ran. It was, however, a real dream to me. The dream being, to convert this slow, top heavy, unattractive little-old-lady's cream-puff into a screaming, low slung sports car. To accomplish this would require replacing the metal body with a new, racing-style Fiberglas shell and hopping up the engine.

Almquist bodied, Crosley powered sports car

98

The advertisements for the plastic body in the magazine declared that the average installation time was fourteen hours. They lied. My father surely knew this because what could a fifteen-year-old, sans license, do with a real sports car?

I looked to my right

And there sat Bev in his Chev

Ah revin' 'er up. . .

By the time I had stripped the sedan to the bare chassis the Fiberglas body arrived. There were no instructions, just a shell and a copy of the invoice showing that the amount of $295.00 had been paid. For the finished car to look right and handle correctly the frame would have to be "Z'd" and "C'd" and the engine would have to be moved back and down, stuff I had only read about in hot rod magazines. It took me a full year, but man was it cool.

At the entry gate, we were greeted by one of the Cam-Lifters who immediately put me to work painting, with Bon-Ami shoe polish, number and class on entrant's windows. I was soon relieved so as I could secure a spot in the pits. Once staked out, Laine and I made it over to the timing stand where she got to see the layout from this eagle's-eye view and to meet the announcer, Isky - So nick-named because he always wore Iskenderian Cam t-shirts.

Once up in the tower Isky told me, "We're shorthanded today, so you'll have to work the pit gate."

"Ah, man. Who's going to protect this fine lookin' young thing while I'm on the gate?"

"Why you can just leave her with ole Isky."

"Hey, I wouldn't trust you with my dog," I said, continuing the jesting.

"You don't have a dog, man."

"Got the picture, daddy-o?"

"Okay, I'll tell you what. The cat from the Enquirer is going to be here to take pictures for the paper and I'll set it up so Laine is the one to hand out the trophies to the winners. They'll probably take her picture for the paper and all that stuff."

I looked at Laine. She was shaking her head up and down with a big smile on her face.

"Man, you got me over a barrel."

"Now get to work and leave me alone with this sweet young thing," Isky smiled, putting his arm around Laine.

Climbing down the ladder I got the last put-down in, "Just remember, ole buddy, whatever you'll be doing to my chick up there, I'll be doing to your rod in the pits, ya dig?"

The light turned green,

That Chev looked mean,

But I put my foot down

As if it were bound. . .

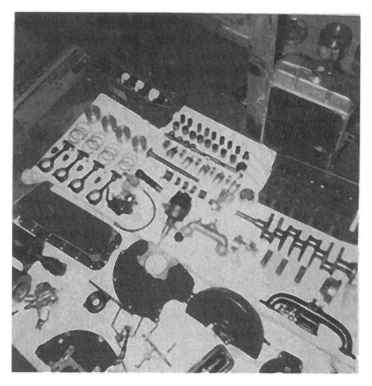

Crosley Engine ready for Assembly

I ended up in the staging area trying to line up the cars and man, was it hot, dirty, dusty and sweaty. Exhaust fumes, burning rubber, swirling clouds of dust engulfed me for the next couple of hours – until I begged relief to get in a few qualifying runs in the "E" Sports Car. The rules were that there had to be at least three vehicles in a class to warrant a trophy. I checked the pits and found three other E/SP – two Crosley Hot-Shots and a brand new Austin-Healey Sprite. I didn't sweat Hot-Shots, but the Sprite had a bigger engine and I didn't know how fast it would be. All of them were heavier than my Fiberglas bodied sports car, plus I had a Harmon-Collins full-race cam and a few other goodies under the hood. The hopped up engine went off the scale of a 10K RPM Stewart-Warner tach!

Two qualifying runs and another stint in the staging area led to my first competition – the Sprite. With a 5.11 rear gear, I easily got him off the line; however, as we approached the traps his 948 cc engine was coming on strong – but not strong enough. For the trophy run, I effortlessly pulled away from one of the Hot-Shots, doubled clutched into2nd, let her wind all the way out past 10,000 RPM and then ducked down behind the tiny windscreen after double clutching the crash-box into third. I grinned all the way back on the dirt return strip to get a trophy from my girl. Life doesn't get any better!

> *Then as I shifted from*
>
> *Strange range to queer gear,*
>
> *I shed a little tear for Bev and his Chev.*

This Regional Meet was captured on 8mm film and has been posted to youtube:

http://www.youtube.com/watch?v=cTo8ddJoIms

There are two films on this site; the first portion being the Regional Meet. I'm sure of the date because I have a trophy, just like the ones shown on the trophy table. The date engraved is 14 Sep 1958 and the trophy girl was my girl. In addition, I have the newspaper clipping from 15 Sep 1958 showing her handing out the trophies.

The next week at the Knights' meeting we were all standing around the bare rails of our club dragster and everyone seemed enthused, that is until, Gil, our president, passed out tickets we would have to sell for the club dance. To build this awesome machine we would individually have to cough up the bread if we didn't sell enough tickets. We were aiming for the "C" class as our engine was a six cylinder Jimmy. We figured we could get more trophies than competing against the big V8s. Well, that and the 6-banger was donated by a local junk yard and one of the guys had made a 3-carb log-type intake manifold.

Chuck Klein, age 16, Spring 1958

The dragster project took up two bays of our 6-bay club garage. Two others were currently being used by members for their own work; Bill was adding a set of two-fours, dual point distributor and a 097 Duntov high-lift cam in his '55 two-tone black & white Chevy sedan with primer spots where he had removed the hood and trunk emblems. Next to him, Sam was replacing the fuel pump on his Caddy powered '49 Mercury – a Merc-o-Lac. It was nosed and decked, but the entire car was painted in gray primer.

You gotta' love me, Baby
And love my hot rod.
Moon caps, three-twos and 4-1-1
- That's all I got!
Don't ya love me, Baby
Even though that's all I got?

After the meeting, and though it was a school night, I followed some of the guys - in my '57 Ford two-door Custom - to Carter's drive-in for a Coke. There I joined Big Bart in his '35 Ford many-door.

"Long time no see," I said, climbing in the front seat.

"Yeah, no lie. I've been keeping my nose to the old grindstone. Between work and this damn night school, I haven't had time to see Janice or work on the '49 or anything. What have you been doing besides pounding your puddin'?"

"Hey, man, I dig ya 'bout school. Now, they've got me going to religious school on Saturday and regular Sunday school on Sunday for my confirmation."

"Oh yeah? I was confirmed, it was a pain in the ass," Big Bart said.

"I didn't know you were Jewish."

"I'm not. It was a Catholic confirmation."

"Catholic, eh? You believe in ghosts and stuff?"

"Naw, I'm an agnostic, asshole," BB said.

"Now, I always knew you were an asshole, but I didn't know you were some kind of fancy asshole. What kind of asshole is an agnostic asshole?"

"It's agnostic . . . comma . . . asshole."

"Wow! That's impressive. What's an agnostic comma asshole?" I continued to pretend ignorance.

"Klein! One of these days I'm going to kick that smart ass of yours," Big Bart joked. "An agnostic is one who doesn't necessarily believe in God, but doesn't necessarily not believe either," BB said.

"Hey that's cool. It's sorta like cover your ass on both sides. If, when the time comes and there is a God, then you can say, `Hey man I never said I didn't believe in you'. And if there ain't no God then you can say you were cool all along, right?

"Not to change the subject, but when are we going to finish the forty-nine?" I asked.

"This weekend. I've found a used manifold with six Stromberg 97s all ready to go. Can you come over Saturday afternoon?"

BB's "other" car was a '49 Ford into which I helped him load a Mercury Flathead engine that he had ported, polished and relieved, bored & stroked and installed a full-race Clay-Smith cam.

"Six-deuces? Man this is really gonna be a fine D-Gas machine!

"Remember our discussion on boring out the venturi on my Crosley carburetor and how you thought it wouldn't work? Well, we all know it did. I'm going to do it to the carb on the fifty-seven now that I've got a spare one."

"How'd you come up with a spare carb? BB asked.

"I had a little fire that I forgot to tell ya about. I was testing some nitro methane and it accidently caught fire. The good news is, the insurance company paid for the carb replacement and the repaint of the hood. The really good news is I got to keep the old carb. I cleaned it up, reinstalled it and it works just fine. The only actual damage was the stud for the air cleaner. I cut it off with a hacksaw. Who needs an air cleaner!"

"Why don't you just put a four-barrel on it?"

"I don't have the scratch, man. Besides it's more fun to experiment, especially since the insurance company is payin'".

Soon, Sonja pulled into Carter's in her 1958, 348/Tri-Power Chevy with four-speed and 4.11 rear end. Talk got around to how fast was it and soon the challenge was made to Bubbles. Bubbles, so nicknamed 'cuz of his curly head and perennial laugh, was an apprentice machinist and had just gotten his '52 Olds running – for the second time. He was the kind of hot rodder that believed if boring an engine

100/1000 of an inch over was good, then .125 was better, and if .125 was better then… . Well, after the bore job he fired it up and drove it around the block once before deciding to put water in the radiator. He dropped the hose in the opening and when it didn't seem to be filling, looked into the engine compartment only to see water pouring out of the side of the block. The force of the larger bore had blown out the now - thinner water jacket walls. With another junk yard block – bored slightly less – plus a hot cam, 2-4s and milled heads running through a Caddy/LaSalle transmission with a gear shift rod extended almost to the inside roof of the car a grudge race was set for Sunday at the strip.

Using the milling machine at my father's shop, I bored the venturi of each barrel to equal the size of the butterfly valve ports on my spare carburetor. Before installing the modified carb, using a stop watch, I timed how long it took to go from one point to another on a seldom used highway. After connecting the altered carb and using a borrowed set of number drills, I drilled the jets one size larger at a time until the engine would run. Then it became trial & error to learn which jet size gave the best time on the test highway. It worked! Though power under 20 MPH was slower, once the engine began to wind up, the car was faster. Oh yeah, gas mileage was significantly reduced, but at $.25/gallon for Ethyl, I could handle it.

It wasn't until the third Sunday of June that confirmation was finally over and I could run at the strip. Though my 272 cubic inch "D" Stock Ford pulled a couple of 185/283 Chevys, I lost the trophy run to another Ford with a 292 cube engine. All right so I wasn't exactly stock, but who's going to know to check venturi size?

Ahh, the sound of a flathead soon filled the staging area as Bart powered his '49 to the line for a timing run. He revved the engine; the flagman dropped his arm and the engine revved . . . and the engine revved. The axle broke.

Bubbles' '52 over-bored Olds with the Caddy/LaSalle Transmission not only captured C-Gas, but yanked Sonja's '58 Tri-Power Chevy.

Author's '57 Ford - "I got him off the line"

YouTube of 8mm film shot by author at Beechmont Drag Strip, Summer 1958: http://youtu.be/gIBt4LsFSGI

The highlight of the day, if you're callous enough, was a blown '57 Chev. Blown, as in blown clutch. Some Harry high-schooler, racing the family grocery-getter, sent pieces of the clutch through the floorboard, dash and windshield.

The Knight's dance was a success if you call only one fist fight between one of our guys and a member of the Cam-Lifters. That, and all the booze consumed could have powered half-a-dozen "A" Fuel Dragsters for a couple of quarter miles. I had a date with Suzy, a girl from my class, who, as it turned out, didn't dig hot rodders. We doubled with Isky in his '53 Stude-lac with glas-pacs.

Don't ya love it, Baby
Don't it give you a fit?
Fender skirts, necker's knob,
and a continental kit.
We're gonna get married
Then we'll settle down
As soon as I win
That drag strip crown.

ROCK 'N RODS

1932 Ford 3-Window Coupe

> *Hearing our song while holding hands*
> *I felt my heart pounding, saw her lips quiver;*
> *we were like two full race duce-coupes*
> *all revved up waiting for the drop of the flag.*

THE CARS: We literally lived, ate, slept, and breathed cars. We lived the lives of those depicted in the hot rod magazines and talked, studied and fantasized about cars, cars and cars. We ate with axle grease impregnated fingers, while we sat on dirty garage floors and loved every minute of it. We slept and dreamed of cars and we breathed the fumes of gas and oil, burned or unburned, that were as sweet a smell to us as Bordeaux was to a Rothschild.

On June 6, 1957, the Automobile Manufacturers Association banned race involvement. The ban was more than mere non-involvement in the actual racing. The racing prohibition also meant that auto manufacturers would not supply pace cars, publicize results, advertise speed-related features of their passenger cars, or help anyone involved in auto racing.

There was a very good reason for the ban. Two years prior, in June 1955, at the 24 Hours of Le Mans race, 77 people were killed and many more were injured when the Mercedes-Benz, driven by Pierre Levegh, traveling at approximately 150 mph crashed into the spectators' stand and burst into flames.

This ban was, however, only a gentlemen's agreement meant to keep Congress from enacting legislative restrictions. By 1959 the cuffs were off. Unofficially the Pontiac Motor Division of GM, under Bunky Knudsen, took control of the stock car racing world. While in the drag world, if you were serious about winning "A" Dragster, the Chrysler Hemi was the only ticket.

Nineteen-Fifty-Nine found the country dotted with hundreds of race tracks of all kinds and grandstands that overflowed with spectators. It was, however, the last hurrah – the beginning of the end of an era. Maybe drag racing was becoming ho-hum, or merely the result of competition for leisure time. But, paying spectators were dwindling. In 1949, a 100 HP, flathead Ford, enhanced with dual carbs and twin exhausts was a machine to be reckoned with. By 1959, cars came from the Big-3 factories with hot cams, 4-speed transmissions and multiple carburetors. The onset of a new era had dawned; whoever has the most money wins the race.

> *Those of us*
> *Weaned on rock & roll;*
> *Have had it melded*
> *To our very soul.*

THE MUSIC: 1959 is remembered more by what didn't happen at the strip than what happened in another mode of transportation – the plane crash that killed Buddy Holly, The Big Bopper and Richie Valens. Rock & Roll and hot rodding are as intertwined as a wrist pin is to a piston, a ring gear to a pinion or a valve to a keeper.

The crash happened on a Tuesday night, but by early Wednesday morning the whole world knew. The date, February third, would eat like battery acid in every teenager's heart. This generation had never experienced any unifying tragedy such as war, famine or the death of a public figure. These hot-rodding, rock & rollers were babies when FDR died - nothing catastrophic had ever occurred in their lifetime. Until now. To the War Baby generation it was devastating.

A pall fell over entire high schools – country-wide. Kids, mostly girls, were crying on each other's shoulders and walking around in a daze. The songs these masters of youthful passions sang not only entertained, but exposed innermost feelings. They knew how kids felt - they knew what they dreamed. Singer Don McLean would memorialize Holly, Valens and Richardson in the 1972 Number 1 hit, "American Pie." He refers to that tragic night as "the day the music died."

> *James Dean and YAKETY-YAK*
> *and a screamin' tenor sax.*
> *Three-twos and spinner caps,*
> *drive-ins and glass packs.*

In 1989, while writing CIRCA 1957, I wanted to include lyrics to period songs to help set the tone for certain scenes. I sent letters to the registered copyright holders of these songs and all but one responded. The replies were generally to dictated the wording for the credits page and some asked for a small fee. The holdout was Chuck Berry. Three unanswered letters later, I called the number registered as the copyright owner of "Maybellene". After being rebuffed by the person answering the phone, I requested to speak to the manager. A gruff voice came on the line and when pressed for permission, he finally said, okay, but the cost is $10,000. For a book that was only scheduled for an initial press run of 3500, that was prohibitive. I asked this manager, why such a high cost when Elvis' agency only wanted $10? The man said, "I've got nothing to show for my years of hit records because people have been taking advantage of me all along and I'm not selling any permissions for peanuts." There was dead silence until, clearing my throat, I meekly demanded, "Who am I talking to?" The voice on the other end: "Mister Berry."

I was in awe of whom I was having a live conversation with. I thanked him and promised not to use his lyrics. The song was central to a particular chapter; therefore, I described the song's story instead.

The car-intensive music was so important it was inseparable from us, the teen-age hot-rodders. "Maybellene" and others such as "Black Denim Trousers," and "Tell Laura I love Her," were scenarios we daydreamed about.

Ahh, girls and hot rods; hot rods and girls. Nothing, absolutely nothing summed it up better than Chuck Berry's unofficial national anthem of the time: "Maybellene!" I mean it had everything: An untrue woman who is caught by a V8 Ford, high speed on the open road, and a beat that made you want to get up and dance. The lyrics entwined a jilted lover in pursuit of his heart throb, Maybellene. His overheating hot rod loses ground to her Cadillac - until it begins to rain. After the rain cools his engine, the heartsick hot rodder finally catches the Caddy at the top of a hill where he wails the rhetorical questions of unfaithfulness.

The consensus was that a Cadillac, being the quality car that it was, would run a long way at a hundred miles per hour, but a Ford, even a V-8 Ford wouldn't. Hopping up a car for the quarter mile drag was one thing. But, it was entirely unrealistic to expect a hopped-up engine to stay cool at sustained high speed. The Ford had to have been a flat-head, as early overhead valve mills were dogs.

Black Denim Trousers & Motorcycle Boots, a top 10 one-hit-wonder by the Cheers, tells the story of a guy with "a hopped up 'cicle that took off like a gun." His girl pleads and begs him not to ride, but "He loved that doggone motorcycle best." He takes off saying he'll ride a thousand miles before the sun sets, but, he has a slight mishap with a train " . . . and when they cleared the wreckage, all they found, was his Black Denim Trousers and Motorcycle Boots. . . ." This song was the inspiration for my story, Record Run. The tough guy, outlaw type was an infatuation of all of us – girls and boys – and still is. Today, we witness the huge proliferation of Harley Davidson riders all decked out as bad-boy wannabees.

Tell Laura I love her: Here, the protagonist, desperate for money to buy his girl, Laura, a wedding ring, calls her on the phone to tell her he'll be late. However, he can only reach her mother to whom he wails the song's title. He enters a stock car race . . . "'Round the track they drove at a deadly pace". The car crashes and with his dying words, again the song's hook, Tell Laura I love her. This Ray Peterson story made it into the top ten.

These important set-of-wheels songs inspired others, including the Beach Boys, to produce the next generation's classics such as Little Deuce Coupe and Fun, Fun, Fun, one of their biggest successes. Jan & Dean's 60s smash hits The Little Old Lady From Pasadena, Drag City and Dead Man's Curve were all long on drag strip talk . . . "The guys come to race her from miles around, But she'll give 'em a length, then she'll shut 'em down".

Idols, girls and careers come and go
as do words to a hit song,
but hot rodders needs for speed
are pure and forever life long

THE PEOPLE: Contrary to some beliefs, hot rodding and rock music didn't begin with the Baby Boomer Generation, the crux of which has loosely been defined as those born between 1945 and 1955. Though this huge influx is most populous and produced the leaders of the anti-war, promiscuity and drug cultures they are more noted as the kids who ushered in the Beatles era and the beginning of hard and acid rock. They were the ones flooding the tarmac at Fab-4 arrivals and over-whelming security at hotels, concerts or anywhere the invaders from Britain were rumored to be. The oldest of the Boomers didn't turn sixteen until 1961; the youngest in 1971, well after the recession of the late 1950s. With fresh money and an improved economy their daddies could buy them a factory car that was faster than anything their older siblings had built by hand.

The War babies (born 1941-1945) excluded themselves from the phenomena of the Beatles and the wave of new music. They felt more mature, as in; to embrace the new music meant mixing with and accepting the values of this younger generation - the Boomers were just kids to them. They surely didn't see themselves bouncing up and

112

down alongside their baby brothers and sisters. Factory muscle cars, however, didn't deter their interest in drag racing, but marriage and all the money-consuming comes-with things surely did.

Kinship to hot rodding was and still is different from music, education and employment inasmuch as age or sex doesn't matter; we all cheer on the racers, builders and tuners of fast cars regardless of their age or ours.

THE STRIP: Early fall 1960 finds my buddy, Jimmy, in possession of a brand new '61, 348 Tri-power, Chevy Convertible with 4-speed and 4.11 Posi-traction (thanks to his daddy). Yeah, it was fast, but he couldn't pull my '60 Vette – at least not with him driving – and that was the rub. Blue-eyed, tow-headed Jimmy was one of those kind of guys the chicks swooned over, but when it came to racing he didn't have that touch; the feel for engine, traction and speed. Somehow he felt he needed a trophy to enhance his chick magnetism and thus a plan was formed.

Sunday, at the local drag strip and after getting classified as Super Stock, we picked a spot in the pit area to pull the hub caps, remove the spare tire, jack, fender skirts and the air filter. Jimmy had fun taking a few trial runs; then it was my turn to practice. I beat his time by a full second and it was decided (as I knew it would be) that I would drive his car in competition.

I had advanced the timing just a tad the day before and over inflated his front tires along with adding a quart of nitro methane to the partially filled fuel tank. I had no idea if the nitro would do good or harm, but it was worth the try.

Meanwhile, I had also prepared my Vette for the strip by giving it a wash and wax job. I mean it was built for road racing with a 3.70 real axle and three-deuces in lieu of the standard two-fours. My strategy was to bolt on the hard top and run Altered Coup – not Modified Sports car class. This way, I figured there would be fewer entrants and thus a better chance of securing a trophy. Back then, if you had a hard top and a modified engine, you could choose between (If you look closely at the photo, you can see C/A on the window – I'm in the near lane with the white wheels).

Author's 1960 Corvette (near lane) at Beechmont Drag Strip, 1961

In addition to the 3-2s, metallic brake linings, HD shocks, quick steering and other road racing improvement, I had recently added a high voltage Mallory coil and stranded-copper spark plug wires. On a whim, while I was playing around in the garage one night, I turned out the lights and watched the engine run in the dark. Sparks were all over the place! Voltage was leaking from plug wire to plug wire and to any metal close by. This prompted me to cover each wire with neoprene fuel line. I slit the line and slipped the wire inside and then wrapped each wire with electrician's tape. What a huge difference in performance that little trick made.

Super Sport class that day had numerous entries, but one particular two-door Biscayne was blowing all contestants away – at least off the line. I was able to work my way through the preliminaries with Jimmy's Impala and finally ended up running the Biscayne for the trophy. He had me off the line as he had done to all others, but as I slammed into third and to my utter amazement, I was not only gaining on him, but he appeared to be slowing down! I pulled him by a full car length and Jimmy got the chick magnet.

Next class up, Altered Coupe. Lucky me, there was only a few entrants and in the trophy run I dusted another Vette off for my statuette. I don't remember the ET, but my best speed was 99 point

114

something – good enough to garner a trophy more than once against cars with 4.11 or 4.56 rear gears (That's me with the trophy atop the car – I still have the trophy).

Author with trophy atop his 1960 Corvette

As Jimmy was reinstalling the hub caps, I wandered over to the cat who was loading his stuff into the Biscayne to ask what happened. He told me he was, ah . . . not exactly stock having a stroker kit and mild cam. He then related that, because he was so much faster than the other cars in the preliminaries and practice runs, he had always backed off so as not to attract attention and get protested. But, during the trophy run he decided to let it all hang out. Halfway down the strip, and still at full throttle, the carburetors just ran out of gas – the stock fuel pump wouldn't handle the added HP and that's when I smoked him.

The Late 50s into the early 60s was the transition era: The music, the cars and especially the people were changing. Man had escaped gravity, the variety of cars and their options was exponentially expanding, the recession was over, a new, younger and hatless

President with a stylish First Lady was adding to the transformations we were about to experience. Life was as good as mom's PBJ – only we had so much more to choose from.

> *Teens, cars and rock & roll*
> *Drives us into a rage;*
> *We're all on the same page.*

EARLY ROAD RACING

Author's 1960 Corvette with custom grille and trophy collection

Preface: The following Road Racing escapades are about racing on public streets and highways – narrow roads that were void of white edge lines and reflective warning signs – in the days just prior to the Interstate expressway system. The cars, during this era (1958-1961), were sans radial tires, disk brakes or power steering.

110 MILES IN 110 MINUTES - 1958

The hands on the suburban Cincinnati clock tower showed seven-ten as we, Hard riding shotgun and Jimmy in the back to watch for cops, headed north. Hard, whose real name was Howard, was so nick-named because that's the way the Kentuckians he worked with at the gas station pronounced Howard. These are the same country boys that used a 'ranch' to work on cars in the 'gruge'. Hard was invaluable in knowing when to pass on the right in the little towns that we roared through. He seemed to sense the power of the little V8 in relation to the allotted passing space. Jimmy was the kind of guy that could charm anything from anyone – we were a skilled team.

Traffic was moderate as we sped out State Route three, weaving in and out of the cars that got in our space. Hitting the first stretch of two lane highway just outside the city limits a long line of cars greeted us. But, good fortune was in our favor as nothing was coming the other way. I pulled over the center line floored the gas pedal, locking the Ford-O-Matic in passing gear, and shouted, "Pick a number from one to ten."

Jimmy yelled back, "Nine."

"Count 'em," I said, as we started to pass them all.

We got to eight before we had to duck back in behind the lead car, a '51 Studebaker. When the path was once again clear we shot around the Studebaker and leveled off at ninety. The Ford was running like a charm.

Our luck was still holding. We had only caught a few stop lights so far and hadn't even seen a cop. It was just getting dark when we came out of Washington Court House and hit the long straight, flat stretches; this was the easy leg. Traffic was still fairly light by today's standards and, at times, I could hold the car at ninety for the four to five miles between towns and villages while passing everything that was moving and some that were not. All except one.

For the longest time there was a set of tail lights that we were barely gaining on. Maybe it was a State Cop, trying to clock us from the front. Too late now. We pressed on. A few miles south of Grove City we caught him. It was a '58 Plymouth Fury that had slowed down, we guessed, to see if we were the law. When I tried to pass, he picked up the pace and within a mile we were nose to tail at a hundred and fifteen! The most the '57 had ever done before was about one-oh-seven, but riding the slipstream of the Fury we could go as fast as he could - without even having to hold the gas pedal to the floor. But every time we tried to pass and hit the full force of the wind, even at full throttle, the little Ford would slow down and then we'd have to fight to get back in the slipstream. It was like this all the way to Grove City, where the Plymouth turned off with a wave of the hand. Now it was the home stretch. We hit High Street and Hard noted the time at eight fifty-two, but we still had a few miles to Broad Street, the center of town. Traffic increased and we caught a few lights. It seemed agonizingly slow after the high speed we had been used to. Finally, downtown Columbus was in sight: Time: nine o'clock sharp! One hundred and ten miles 110 minutes!! Let 'em try an beat that! We were all ecstatic and a little relieved, too. Being part of history is always worth every risk and cold sweat.

The '57 Ford with other family cars: My Sister's '56 Vette, my Mother's '58 Cadillac convertible and the almost finished Almquist-bodied Crosley I built during my 16th year. Photo date was early spring, 1958.

THE 270 COP CAR - 1958

That was on a Friday night. By Monday, another kid in a '58 Dodge cut school to try to best my time (he couldn't do it). Meanwhile Jimmy, Hard and I skipped school in an attempt to establish a Cincinnati to Lexington, KY record. South bound we made a few wrong turns, filled up with gas - cheaper in KY - and seemed to see a cop every mile or so. Well, we'll set the record coming home.

We were in Jimmy's '58 Impala convertible with the 348 big block and 4-barrel, but a glider for a transmission. Taking U.S. 27 North, which was better road than U.S. 25, and with Hard driving we were making excellent time roaring through one little burg after another.

We had to be averaging at least seventy coming out of Lexington as we hadn't had a stop until we hit Paris – Kentucky, not France.

On the far side of Cynthiana we hit a stretch of three lane road. Hard decided it was time to see what the big Impala would do, pushing the needle to over a hundred, the canvas top ballooning high over their struts. No sooner had we pulled to a stop in the next town than a cop pulled next to us. No one had seen him. He leaned over, rolled down his passenger window, motioning for Hard to do the same. The cop car was a 1957 Chev with red lights in the grille and the unmistakable sound of a two-seventy engine loping under the hood. "Say boys," the cop began in a slow southern drawl. "Ya'll goin'a bit fast back there weren't ya?"

Hard didn't know what to say. Nobody did. The cop continued, "Now I'll tell ya what I want 'chew to do. Ya'll just turn that there machine around and follor me back to the Court House. I rightly believe the Judge jest might want to have a talk with ya'll. Ya hear?"

Hard acknowledged the command as politely as possible, and we began the trip back to Cynthiana. Following the cop, we ran through our options. We could try to out run him by turning off at the next intersection, claim one of us was sick and we were trying to get to a hospital, or that the gas pedal stuck. As the miles rolled by, we realized that anything we tried would be just plain dumb.

The Court House, and its inhabitants, was right off a "Saturday Evening Post" cover. It looked like Norman Rockwell had made the whole thing, with its giant stone construction, dark woodwork and big white, globe-shaped light fixtures that hung from the high ceilings. The clerk and bailiff were both rosy cheeked and bright eyed, one wearing bib overalls, the other a short vest over his huge belly. The Judge looked like a hold-over from the "Grapes of Wrath," with his fat unshaven face, a cigar in the corner of his mouth and big wide suspenders stretched over an ivory colored undershirt which partially covered his hairy chest. As the officer ushered us into the court room, a middle aged woman hurriedly got down from the Judge's bench where she had been sitting and walked out the back door, straightening her skirt as she went. The officer spoke as the Judge swiveled around in his high back chair to face us, "Yer Honor, these here boys was ah goin' faster than the duly posted legal speed limit."

120

"How fast were they going, Ernie?" The Judge asked.

"Don't rightly know, yer Honor, but I was ah goin' a plum over ah hundred and twenty and I was ah barely catchin' 'em. Had to chase 'em clear to the light at the County Road."

"How old are you boys and why aren't you in school?" Demanded the Judge.

"We're all about sixteen, sir, and we didn't have school today, Hard volunteered.

"No school? Where in tarnation do you go to school. This ain't no holly-day, is it?"

"No sir. We're from Cincinnati and it's a teacher's day."

He bought it. So far so good.

"Well, if you want to plead guilty and pay the clerk a hundred dollars you can drive real slow outta here."

We huddled only to discover that all we had between us was twenty two dollars and change. Hard, now the official spokesman stepped forward, "Your Honor, all we have is twenty dollars between us, but if you'll let us go we'll send the rest of it as soon as we get home, honest."

"Just pay the clerk the twenty dollars – as your bond that you'll show up Saturday for your trial jist like it says on the ticket." Then turning to the officer, the Judge continued, "Ernie I want you to escort these young boys to the town limit, and I also want you to radio ahead to the State Po-lice that they're a-coming through."

RACE TO BIG BOY -1959

Following an impromptu baseball game on a hot July night, a bunch of us decided to cool off in my parent's swimming pool. My '57 Ford 2-door Custom was second into the driveway of our suburban home, nosed into the front of Sammy's 1957 Chevy convertible with PG and the 185 HP engine.

Around midnight the house lights flashed telling us party time was over. Nothing was said, but no one wanted to be the last one to the Big Boy. I backed out of the driveway knowing if I tried to turn around, Sammy would have the lead – so I backed about a half mile, with the convertible on my front bumper, before giving it up and bouncing over a curb to make the turn-around. Now it was catch up time as we both ran at speeds over 60 in the 25 zone. Approaching the green traffic light at Reading Road, It was clear Sammy would make the light and head southbound. I knew from experience if I took the side street the next light would be green for me and red for Sammy.

At this next light here comes the Chevy, top down, horn blaring and a big grin on Sammy's face as he slammed through the red lighted intersection. Now, we diced with light traffic for the next couple of miles on this 4-lane city street. The final light just before the Big Boy found me first in line and next to an old guy in a '48 Ford four-door sedan. Upon the change of the light, I figured, I'd box Sammy in by matching the '48s speed right up to final second and then I'd pass the '48 and ease into the restaurant's right side entry. Sammy prowled back and forth trying to find an opening as the distance closed. Suddenly, I heard the Powerglide kick into passing gear as Sammy rocketed over the double-yellow line and abreast of me. I down shifted and tromped the throttle. At the last instance, I locked up the brakes and literally slid and bounced into the parking lot as Sammy overshot and roared into the exit drive. The old guy, at a stately pace of 25 MPH, sauntered by shaking his fist at us.

> Fuel filled veins of a carburetor
> or oil in the journals of a bearing,
> is as blood is to the arteries of men
> who live for speed and daring.

FLORIDA, HERE WE COME

It was a rainy Thursday night in the spring of 1960 as I tried doing my Trig homework, but I couldn't figure it out. This was near the end of my senior year of high school and in this class, I was hopelessly behind. I got into my 2-week old birthday present, a new 1960 Corvette, and drove to Roselawn, a Cincinnati suburb, hoping to find a shoulder to cry on. Jimmy's Vette was in the lot at the Center

Pharmacy, so I stopped in to join him at the soda fountain. The Zap was also there and Hard came by a few minutes later, making it a foursome to commiserate. Without any previous conscious thought I said, "The weather's miserable, Donna tossed me for another cat, my grades aren't what you'd call cherry, and my parents are going to take my Vette away as soon as they get back from vacation. I think I'll go to Florida. Anybody want to come along?"

"You mean Florida, where the sun always shines and it's not so damn cold?" Hard asked.

"That's the place."

"Sounds good to me. When do we leave?"

"Can you be ready in half an hour?"

"No sweat," Howard answered, as both our spirits began to soar

"Now listen, man. I'm serious. I want to go there and not come back. I figure we can get our grades transferred to a high school down there and get jobs and just live there. I don't want to . . . wait make that, I can't come back if I leave, ya dig."

"I'm hep. That's the only way I could go too. If I leave I'll never be able to come back either," Howard solemnly stated.

"How much bread you got? I've got about a hundred at home," I said.

"I have at least that much. How 'bout you guys coming up with a little scratch, say maybe a sawbuck each. It ought to be worth that much just to be rid of us," Hard said, in a joking way, but the Zap and Jimmy forked it over.

"Okay, everything's set. Cohen, if you'll take Hard home to pack, I'll get my stuff and meet you guys at the Cities Service station in half an hour."

It was nine-thirty when we pulled onto Reading Road for what was sure to be the last time. We hadn't even talked about a final destination because we didn't want anyone to know. But once in the privacy of the tiny cockpit of the Vette, I suggested, "How's Tampa-St. Pete sound?" And without waiting for an answer, I continued. "I checked the atlas at home and it looks like we can follow U.S. 27 all the way to Atlanta and then pick up U.S. 41 which is direct to the Gulf Coast and . . . beaches, sunshine and babes. I don't think we

123

should go to Miami because that's the first place they look for run-a-ways. What do you think?"

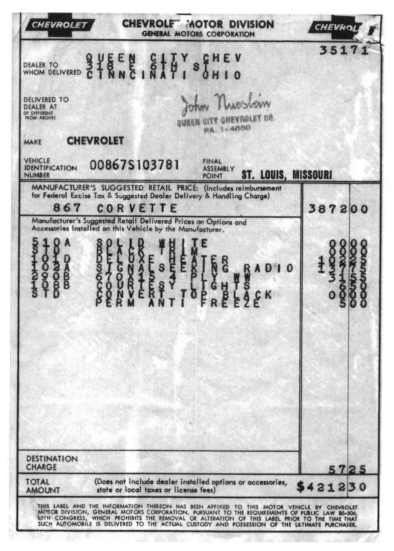

Original Window Sticker for Author's 1960 Corvette

"Any place in Florida is alright with me, just wake me when we're there, ol' buddy," Hard sighed, as he snuggled into his coat-turned-pillow.

"Ol' buddy, my ass! You're going to have to do your share of the driving, too.

This basic sports car was equipped with the standard 283 V-8 with four-barrel carburetor and a 3-speed close-ratio transmission. Though 2nd and 3rd gears were synchronized, first gear, like most cars of the era, was not. In order to shift into 1st, without grinding the gears (and possibly damaging them), you either had to come to a complete stop or double clutch – a technique not familiar to many. The trick is to bring the shift lever into neutral, let the clutch out, and rev the engine to match the RPM the engine would be running at that road speed. In other words, if , say 40 MPH = 4000 RPM in 1st gear, then, with the clutch out and the transmission in neutral, run the engine up to 4000, shove the clutch in again and pull the shift lever into 1st gear. Practice and a 'good ear/feel,' it is quite fast and can even be done without a tachometer or even using the clutch.

Once through Newport, the traffic thinned out and I could really let the Corvette roll down the short straights and around the countless turns through the semi-mountainous hills of Kentucky. The almost-walking speed limit of sixty, which we had to adhere to when behind some old fogy, was frustrating and agonizing. Hell, the Vette could almost do that in first gear! But to me, every car I passed and every curve I entered was a challenge, a challenge to drive to the limit. I loved it. I loved feeling the brakes hauling the beast to a safe speed, the double-clutching down into first for tight bends and then the surge of raw power as I opened her up coming out of the corners. I relished the exhilaration of passing a string of cars at red line in second gear. I felt the machine and I were one, and at times I was so intent on the task at hand I was totally unaware of anything, including my passenger. It wasn't until we were deep into the Bible belt that I began to slack off. The quad head lamps had no trouble finding the small, old and rusty signs peering out of the brush from between Burma-Shave jingles and Mail Pouch sided barns: "PREPARE TO MEET THY MAKER". It's not that I'm not a religious person, but those ominous signs had a very sobering effect. At least for a few miles, anyway.

It was in these dips, valleys and twisty two-laners that I came to realize a passing technique: If he can go, I can go. In other words, if a car, say three in front of me in a line of cars, pulls out to pass, I could also move into the on-coming lane even if it was over a double-yellow line. As long as I could see the other passing car, I knew it had to be clear for me. Strings of cars, back then, almost always kept at least 4-5 car lengths apart to allow for those wishing to pass to tuck in.

The only cop we saw was on a straight stretch just outside Atlanta. He was parked off the side of the road among a cluster of pines and took off after us as we sailed by at the usual 90 MPH clip. Hard was driving and as soon as we crested a small hill and were out of his sight, Howard panic-stopped, as I braced myself against the chicken bar. During some of our brief conversations over the past eight hours or so we had planned for such a situation. As soon as we stopped we both got out and took off our shirts. Standing there in our T-shirts, we watched with subdued glee as the State Trooper overshot us. The cop had to back up on the shoulder of the road to get to us and was obviously very angry, jamming his hat on as he got out of the patrol car.

"Ya'll goin' a mite fast back there, weren't you, boys?" The Trooper snarled as he looked us over.

"No sir. If we were going as fast as you we couldn't have gotten stopped this quickly, sir," I said, in my most sincere and innocent voice.

"Don't smart mouth me boy, and which one of you was ah drivin'?"

"Gee, I don't remember. Whose turn was it to drive? Do you remember, Howard?"

"Why no, I'm not sure, maybe… ."

"Alright boys, I'm trying to be patient, now which one was driving because he's going to jail and the other one can then go on his way. Now, come on, and fess up. Ya hear."

Howard and I looked him right in the eye, but didn't say a word. We had him. He couldn't write a ticket unless he could place one of us behind the wheel and since we both had dark hair and white shirts there was no way he could honestly say who was driving. We were lucky he was an honest cop. He checked his hot sheet to see if the Vette was reported stolen and finally sent us on our way with the admonishment, "Ya'll drive slow now. We don't cotton to no Yankees racing through our fine State, ya here."

We crashed the Florida State line and stopped to put the top down. This was really living. Of course, in less than fifty miles we had to put the top back up due to the buffeting of the wind at ninety per. It wasn't until we hit the city limit sign of St. Pete, that we could put it down again and soak up some of that glorious sunshine. It was one-thirty-five in the afternoon; 1015 miles since we left our former home on the Ohio River – an average of 62.5 MPH. Within a few minutes of that momentous occasion, we pulled up next to two chicks walking on a sidewalk. Hard didn't waste a minute. "Hi. I wonder if you two good lookin' girls could help us out?"

They looked at each other, giggled, and then walked over to the car. Howard continued, "We just got in from the North, the cold, cold North, and we need directions to the beach. I've just gotta wiggle my toes in the surf."

"Well," the taller of the two began. "If you take this… ."

"That sounds too complicated. Why don't you two just hop in and show us," Howard interrupted and then continued. "My name's Howard and this is my buddy, Chuck, and we sure would appreciate a little southern hospitality in showing us the way to the ocean."

The taller one giggled again and then spoke once more. "I've never ridden in a Corvette. Can we all fit in there? Will you bring us back? We can't be gone long."

This time I spoke. "Sure there's plenty of room if one of you sits on Howard's lap. We'll bring you back whenever you say, if you can keep us from getting lost. So hop in."

"Well, okay, but we can't be gone long. Cecilia, you go and tell Mom that we'll be right back. That's Cecilia, she's my sister, and I'm Barbara," the tall one said.

Sixteen hours and five minutes after leaving the soda fountain we each had a chick on our arm and were lying on a genuine, authentic and actual beach! Barb and I were hitting it off real good, even doing a little kissy face. Howard and Cee didn't seem to be having any trouble getting to know each other either. Man, life doesn't get any better than this.

Within 24 hours, we had both found jobs – Hard in a gas station and me parking cars at a swank hotel/restaurant. Paradise, however, doesn't last forever – or even a week. It wasn't long before the SPPD arrested us for grand theft auto. The car was titled in my father's name and he pressed charges.

The city jail was nothing like juvenile detention where I had, ah, spent a little time back home. This was big time; eight double, steel bunks in each cell with bars and smelly, scruffy men everywhere. There were already seven in the cell I was assigned, so I immediately climbed onto the only vacant bunk and strived to emulate tough and cool. Trying to act nonchalant, I pulled a cigarette from the pack rolled up in my sleeve and lit up. Hey, I had it made. I was one of the guys. All I had to do was look cool and keep blowing smoke. I finished the fag and casually tossed the butt in the toilet just below my bunk. Within a second, one of the hardened criminals I shared this home-sweet-home with, jumped up and grabbed me by the shirt front. Fish breath, his scarred unshaven face, inches from mine belched out, "Listen punk, around here we pass the butts onto the next guy. We don't never throw 'em in no shit can. Understand?"

"Sure, sure, man, I can dig that. I'm, I'm, I'm sorry. Here do you want my whole pack?" I said, meekly reaching for my shoulder.

"No, asshole. Just pass the butts on, okay?"

In juvenile there was nothing to do but stare at the walls and sleep. Here I was afraid to sleep as I had seven other guys watching me watch them. Sleeping on a flat steel plate with holes in it, and nothing but a dirty blanket for a cover, was not conducive to good rest. However, I managed to cop a few Z's and woke up feeling a little better, especially since I hadn't been robbed, raped or beaten, by my bunk mates.

Breakfast was served in a large room on steel tables with steel benches for seats. Everything was steel, even the cups which the prisoners banged on the table top until coffee was served. A big fat colored man with one gold tooth in an otherwise toothless mouth, passed out the trays of food and kept the coffee cups filled. I ate the

128

yellow stuff that was supposed to be scrambled eggs, but tasted sort of like salted chalk dust with maybe a little pepper. The toast was great and the coffee better, but as hungry as I was, I couldn't handle the grits.

By early afternoon Eddie - that's the guy who had grabbed me by the shirt - and I had become jail house buddies. I told him I was up for Grand Theft Auto and he said he was in for Armed Robbery, but he didn't think they could make the charge stick because he had tossed the gun he used into the bay. He told me he was from somewhere up north, where he had a wife and two kids. He also said that he was almost thirty, but had spent six of those years in the big house for burglary. He looked at least fifty, with scars and tattoos all over his body and all his front teeth were missing. Somewhere around three, they came and got me. As I walked out, not knowing if I'd be back, I tossed the remainder of my fags to Eddie who gave me a big toothless grin and said he'd save them for me in case I was sent back.

After that night in the slammer, lawyers bargained for the charges to be dropped if we promised to be good boys. Hard's parents arranged for him to fly home and my mom who had flown down, chaperoned me all the way to Cincinnati! But hey, that trip down at an average of 62 mph will live on.

Put a gallon in me, Alan

THE DIRT TRACK

At 50 +/- MPH, it had to appear that we were hurtling straight for the telephone pole...then at what must have seemed like the absolute last possible moment - as the tires chirped on the hard dirt in a full panic-stop - she was thrown forward, her knuckles white against the black chicken-bar. Suddenly realizing we weren't going to hit the pole, the pony-tailed blonde surely believed we were going to roll. One hand came free as she was slammed against the passenger door, the open roadster making a very hard left while the rear end swung out and the engine revved tight. Surviving all that, and as we headed into the straight-a-way, the 16 year-old was now pinned to the seatback - a prisoner of acceleration.

After three times around, I pulled into the infield and grinned at my passenger, a teen-age honey. She was wide-eyed and as white as my Ermine White Vette. "I, I, I...was never so scared. I thought we were going to hit that pole...and roll over...let's do it again," she stammered. Stop watches in hand, my buddy and the 5/8 mile dirt track owner were striding over excitedly proclaiming that I had broken the track record.

The track was wide enough to allow the technique of the four-wheel- drift. Before ever trying this in my expensive and fast Corvette, I had become somewhat proficient at this technique by practicing in my Almquist bodied Crosley Sports car I had built during my 16th year and on snow covered parking lots in a 1957 Ford.

This was early summer, 1960, and I was still getting the feel of my combination 18th birthday gift and high school graduation present, a new 230 HP, 3-speed (close-ratio) Corvette with options of AM Push-Button radio, White-wall tires and heater. The cost was $3433.01. The track, laid out in some farmer's field, was near Middletown, about an hour north of Cincinnati. It was the only place around that permitted anyone with a driver's license to race. Passengers were also allowed - this in the days long before the proliferation of lawyers that got into everything. I loved road racing, but being only 18 years old SCCA was out of the question for three more years.

Post-graduation, and against my parent's wishes, I took a job instead of going to college. I needed money to build my Vette - I mean what's more important, playing Joe College with a stocker or having a fast machine?

THE BUILD

During the rest of the summer, as funds permitted, I added: Marchal headlamps, quick steering adapter, HD shocks, metallic brake linings, 4-speed transmission, HD clutch, three two-barrel carburetors on an Edelbrock manifold, Duntov 098 cam with solid lifters and a dual point distributor.

Sure, this stuff was expensive and it took every dime I earned, but I was living at home and had a pal whose father owned a garage. He had given me the garage's vender's number thus allowing me to purchase all Chevrolet parts at a 40% discount.

1 Four speed transmission $254.56

1 Heavy duty clutch $30.21

4 Heavy duty shocks $29.40

4 Sets, metallic brake linings $35.21

1 Quick steering adapter $11.33

1 Dual point distributor $40.40

1 Duntov 098 Camshaft $22.43

1 Set solid lifters $21.17

1 Set of gaskets $12.18

3 Two barrel Rochester carbs $54.88

1 Edelbrock intake manifold $53.20

1 Fuel block and fittings $28.49

2 Marchal head lamps $14.20

By late summer, I discovered three problems:

1) Hot days and/or racing produced vapor lock;

2) Hard cornering sometimes caused loss of power due to the carburetor float remaining closed because gas was jamming it in the up position;

3) Progressive linkage was not conducive to road racing.

The solution to the last problem was easy. With some scrap steel and the use of the lathe in the machine shop of my father's factory, I rigged straight linkage and set it up to idle on the center carb only. The fix for the other issues came to me in an inspiration. I bought an extra fuel pump (electric) and fuel block. Then I drilled and tapped a hole into the base of each float bowl where I threaded in a ball-check valve and a flow valve. I ran a fuel line back to the fuel tank from the new pump. Now, I had one pump pumping gas into the carbs in the normal fashion, while another pump sucked gas out of the carbs - though restricted by the flow-valve. It took some experimenting with float levels and flow-valve settings, but after I got it worked out I never had vapor lock or "ran out of gas" in a corner again.

The metallic brake linings for the drum brake era were a significant factor. To test them, I found an open stretch of highway in the pre-dawn hours and ran from zero to 100 and back to zero – at a full panic-stop - three times in a row without any brake fade. It took brute force to push this very hard non-power or vacuum assist pedal, but these racing brakes really worked. The heavy duty mechanical clutch also required significant leg muscles - I couldn't hold it in at a stop light for more than 15-20 seconds before my leg would begin to shake. Likewise, power steering was not an option and though the quick ratio alternative was better than standard; it still required more turns lock-to-lock than today's everyday sedans.

THE FOUR-WHEEL DRIFT

The four-wheel-drift was a technique I learned of by reading books and magazine articles long before I was old enough to legally drive. The best how-to instructions came from Denis Jenkinson's excellent accounting of 1950s open road racing, The Racing Driver, the theory and practice of fast driving. As most all cars back then were front engine, rear-wheel-drive they would naturally over-steer (go into a corner hard and the rear end, being lighter, would slide out). To compensate, the driver would have to induce an under-steer condition.

1) You have to be going faster than the car will go around the corner on rails. In other words, you must enter the corner at a speed that the car will not negotiate without sliding off the road or wiping out;

2) It's essential to have enough power to cause the rear wheels to spin;

3) Just before the apex of the turn, crank the wheel hard enough (left for a left-hand corner) to set the front

wheels sliding thus inducing an understeer. If you do nothing at this point, the car will plow off the road;

4) With the car's front end beginning to slide and the middle of the turn coming, pour the coal to her causing the drive tires to spin and the rear end to try to slide out;

5) Now with all four wheels sliding (drifting), correct the steering and control the rear end slide with the throttle. The first few times you try this, it's really hairy – pressing the accelerator while already in a spin is not an instinctive reaction.

On hard pavement, it's mandatory to be in the correct gear and have enough horsepower to spin the tires. Getting into the correct gear when approaching a corner is a trick of heal-toeing – slamming on the brakes with the heal while blipping the throttle with the toe and at the same time ramming the shift lever into the lower gear. Sure it's scary and hard on tires, but very exciting and fun!

MY BUDDY THE CHIEF

Within a day after they finished paving the parking lot to a major new shopping center, I realized it would make a great speedway and opportunity to test my driving skills and the enhancements to the engine and suspension. Using the light poles as pylons, I zigzagged and crisscrossed the Vette circuitously around the Mall, weaving in and out of these pseudo pylons at speeds up to 90 MPH. About the second or third lap of this improvised almost one mile race track, a police car, lights flashing, stopped my fun.

The officer was livid! He had me out of the car and was threatening a trip to the county jail and a tow of my wheels. My shotgun and high school classmate now looked more scared of law enforcement than he was of the laws of physics – the possibility that we would roll or crash. I had noticed his white knuckles on the chicken bar when the Vette was drifting, aiming for and almost hitting the concrete based poles. Now he was visibly shaken. Within a minute another patrol car screeched in. The officer in the second scout car, with the name-tag, Doug Renneker, was also the police chief to the mall's home in this tiny community of Springdale, Ohio.

He immediately proceeded to lash out about how dangerous speed was and other tough talk. Then telling the first officer he'd take care of the incident, sent him on his way. The Chief, with a big smile, then clapped me on the back and asked to see the Vette's engine all to the amazement of my buddy who stood there, mouth agape. It seems Doug was also the part-time truck driver for my father's paper converting business and had taught me how to drive a semi-truck. Of course, he let us go, but made me promise never to speed in his town again. To this day, I've always honored that promise. Thanks again Doug, and thanks for being a positive influence in my life.

> *If you do enough dumb stuff,*
> *lady luck will eventually take pity.*

THE STREET RACE

Late on a summer night in 1961, I noticed my buddy Howard's '57 Chevy in the lot at the White Castle drive-in. Pulling up next to him in my 1960 Corvette, I said, "Hey man, I see you finally got that junker runnin'."

"This "junker" will dust you off any time you're ready," came the reply from Hard (as he was known, 'cuz that's how the Kentuckians he worked with pronounced Howard).

Before I could think of a good come-back, Louie walked over saying, "It's about time you two smoked one off." Howard and I looked at each other and grinned.

Buyers of new Corvettes received a free subscription to CORVETTE NEWS, an official publication of GM. In one of the early issue the factory gave racing tune-up tips – this practice was surely curtailed once the lawyers read it. Nevertheless, Volume 1, Number 2 included upper limit settings such as valve clearances, point/dwell and timing advance calibrations. Utilizing these specifications gave a significant edge over 'stock' tuned engines.

The latest addition to my no-longer-stock Vette was a set of 'lake pipes'- 3" pipe (w/cap) welded to the header pipe. This muffler by-pass created nerve jangling decibels at high rpms and cost me a ticket! I was in route to the dirt track near Middletown when I decided to blow the carbon out. Passing a State Highway Patrol post at full throttle and around 100 MPH got the undivided attention of the OIC who radioed ahead. At the side road leading to the track sat a marked cruiser. He liked the car and sympathized with my plight, but the Lieutenant at the post insisted I be cited.

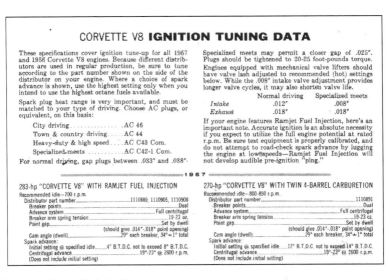

CORVETTE V8 **IGNITION TUNING DATA**

These specifications cover ignition tune-up for all 1957 and 1956 Corvette V8 engines. Because different distributors are used in regular production, be sure to tune according to the part number shown on the side of the distributor on your engine. Where a choice of spark advance is shown, use the highest setting only when you intend to use the highest octane fuels available.

Spark plug heat range is very important, and must be matched to your type of driving. Choose AC plugs, or equivalent, on this basis:

City driving	AC 46
Town & country driving	AC 44
Heavy-duty & high speed	AC C43 Com.
Specialized meets	AC C42-1 Com.

For normal driving, gap plugs between .033" and .038".

Specialized meets may permit a closer gap of .025". Plugs should be tightened to 20-25 foot-pounds torque. Engines equipped with mechanical valve lifters should have valve lash adjusted to recommended (hot) settings below. While the .008" intake valve adjustment provides longer valve cycles, it may also shorten valve life.

	Normal driving	Specialized meets
Intake	.012"	.008"
Exhaust	.018"	.018"

If your engine features Ramjet Fuel Injection, here's an important note. Accurate ignition is an absolute necessity if you expect to utilize the full engine potential at rated r.p.m. Be sure test equipment is properly calibrated, and do not attempt to road-check spark advance by lugging the engine at low speeds—Ramjet Fuel Injection will not develop audible pre-ignition "ping."

=== **1957** ===

283-hp "CORVETTE V8" WITH RAMJET FUEL INJECTION

Recommended idle—700 r.p.m.

Distributor part number	1110889, 1110905, 1110908
Breaker points	Dual
Advance system	Full centrifugal
Breaker arm spring tension	19-23 oz.
Point gap	Set by dwell
	(should give .014"-.018" point opening)
Cam angle (dwell)	29° each breaker, 34°÷1° total
Spark advance:	
Initial setting @ specified idle	4° B.T.D.C. not to exceed 8° B.T.D.C.
Centrifugal advance	19°-23° @ 2600 r.p.m.
(Does not include initial setting)	

270-hp "CORVETTE V8" WITH TWIN 4-BARREL CARBURETION

Recommended idle—800-850 r.p.m.

Distributor part number	1110891
Breaker points	Dual
Advance system	Full centrifugal
Breaker arm spring tension	19-23 oz.
Point gap	Set by dwell
	(should give .014"-.018" point opening)
Cam angle (dwell)	29° each breaker, 34°÷1° total
Spark advance:	
Initial setting @ specified idle	12° B.T.D.C. not to exceed 14° B.T.D.C.
Centrifugal advance	19°-23° @ 2600 r.p.m.
(Does not include initial setting)	

Corvette News, Vol. 1, #2

Hard, with hands on hips in a defiant manner, exclaimed, "I'm ready, if you are."

"Wait a minute. What have you got in this thing? You're too eager. Pop the hood and let me see," I demanded.

"Okay with me. It's just a stock two-seventy."

"Bull! You never drove a stocker in your life."

He opened the hood, but all that was obvious were two-four's. Anything else had to be hidden in the engine. "Fire it up one time, Hard," I insisted.

When the engine caught I could tell by the sound that it had a hot cam, maybe an Isky 5-cycle? "How big did you bore it and what's the cam?" I said, probing for information.

"Now look, do you want to talk or do you want to race?" Howard took a hard line and I knew it was now or never.

"Okay. But no standing start. We go from a roll. I'll take Louie and you get a passenger to count."

Rules agreed, we pulled onto north bound Reading Road, in the Bond Hill suburb of Cincinnati. Leveling off side by side, between twenty-five and thirty, I rolled my window down to hear the count, as Howard's passenger shouted above the din, "One...two...three!"

At the sound of the magic number, I stabbed the throttle and hit the high beam switch, the big Marchal road-racing headlights I'd recently installed lit up the entire four lane road including the 35 mph speed limit sign a quarter mile forward. The sudden acceleration slammed me back in the seat and I fixed one eye on the tach and put my full attention into hearing the engine. I got the jump on him, the three-two's and a lower first gear ratio, having the advantage on the low end. The recent tune up had not been in vain.

In my second gear (a ratio between his first and second) my lead increased, but once into third and as we neared the top of the hill, just before Langdon Farm Road, he began to close the distance - his two-four's and whatever else he had, now had the edge.

Cresting the hill abreast of each other and at a little over a hundred the powerful French headlights picked up the reflective decals of a city police car waiting for the light at Langdon Farm. It was too late now. I could see by the condition of the "walk-wait" signal that the light was about to change to red for our north bound cars. We went through the red light together at something over fifty, hand on horns, high beams bright and engines revved tight. The cop didn't waste any time in turning on his bubble gum machine and pulling out around the line of cars waiting with him. Howard stopped in front of the high school, but I kept right on going while reaching over in front of Louie to hit the switches, that turned out my tail and brake lights. I took the first right and got on it all the way to where it curved around and backed into Langdon Farm. Approaching this intersection, I set up for a four-wheel drift - after seeing that there was no other traffic. The big Vette slid around the bend in perfect control, smoke billowing from the wheel wells as I poured the coal to her. From Langdon Farm we wound our way through the back streets of suburban villages. The last time I saw the cop, he was about a half-mile behind me and losing ground. I wasn't worried about a road block because the city and the villages were on different radio frequencies.

Once at home, I put the Vette in the garage and found a key to my sister's car, which we took back to White Castle. Howard was waiting for us, grinning from ear to ear. He explained how John-law pulled next to him, told him to wait, and took off after me. As soon as the cop was out of sight, Howard merely turned around and drove back to the drive-in. The cop, obviously a rookie, had failed to copy license plate numbers or even get a good look at Hard and we were now both scot free.

YouTube link to 'Through the Windshield' of this Corvette on the open road in 1961, running at 90 mph:

http://youtu.be/KtAYqexKeNE

TRUCKIN' – CIRCA 1960

1951 International Semi-tractor with 32' Steel Trailer

Nineteen-fifty-eight found me sixteen and in possession of a driver's license, an automobile and a girlfriend. Life doesn't get any better than this. However, within two years I had contempt for the automobile, the police and the girl, well . . . maybe it was she who held the contempt. All was not lost. I now longed for the coveted Chauffer license. With that, I could operate semi-trucks - not that I knew how to drive one. As a youngster, I had always fantasized being one of those real men handling these big rigs - backing them into tight spots, squeezing down narrow alleys and, air horns blasting, high-ballin' on the open road.

Ohio Drivers who held the Chauffeur license (now called a Commercial Drivers License or CDL) were required to wear a 1 3/4" badge in a prominent location (usually on one's cap) when driving for hire. In 1960 there were no classes of drivers, if you passed the exam you could drive for hire a taxi, straight truck, semi-truck & trailer - anything legally licensed. The exam consisted only of a written test that asked mostly questions about weights, sizes and vehicle running lights. Medical exams or demonstration of ability to operate a truck were not compulsory. One only had to be 18 years of age and possess a valid Ohio operator's license to qualify.

The week I turned eighteen, I scanned the state booklet, memorized some statistics and, eureka, I'm a truck driver. Immediately thereafter, I stopped by my father's medium sized manufacturing company and told the general manager I was available should they need a backup truck driver. The corporation, The Progress Lithographing Co., had a 1951 International semi with 32' single-axle trailer.

Ohio Chauffeur's Pin, c.1960

He did ask if I knew how to drive it and I assured him, with fingers crossed, I did. He didn't ask how I learned, but since I was the owner's son and had cut the grass of the factory's 12 acre site for the past six summers with a side-sickle bar cutter equipped Farmall, he obviously gave me the benefit of a doubt.

139

Within a month the G.M. called to ask if I could make a rush-job run to Lebanon, Ohio. They needed to deliver about 10 tons printed material in a hurry. It was early morning and I was working on a term paper for my college history class when the call came. Guess who didn't do well in history that semester?

I quickly sought out the company machinist, Obe, who had been most helpful in supplementing the mechanical skills I learned in high school shop classes. I knew Obe had driven the semi in the past, but had purposely allowed his chauffeur license to lapse because he didn't want to drive the truck after spending all day rigging machinery and such into it. The regular driver, the police chief of a nearby suburb, was only part time as there wasn't enough work. Our Cincinnati based paper convertor did most of its business at distances where it was more economical to utilize commercial haulers. Trucking with the company truck was usually just between the company's four plants, all located within 50 miles of each other.

Though the chauffeur's test required knowledge of weights and size limits, I really had no firsthand experience or understanding of how much 10 tons is and what it was like to propel a 32' trailer so loaded.

The tractor had just been serviced and this required hooking it up with the all-steel single-axle trailer. After sliding the fifth wheel onto the king pin, Obe showed me how to attach the glad-hands, where to plug in the trailer lights and how to retract the dolly. It was a rainy afternoon, making my first attempts to back the trailer into the unlighted loading dock more difficult. I did find it easier than backing the short utility trailer behind the company Farmall tractor. It seems, the shorter the trailer, the harder it is to back up.

As soon as the shipping clerk waved that the rig was loaded, I started for the cab, only to have Obe hail me back to the dock. In a fatherly, but firm tone, he told me that it was I, not the loading party, who was responsible for the safety and security of the load. If the load shifts and is damaged or causes an accident, I will be the one held accountable. We walked into the trailer where Obe pointed out how loads should always be placed against the bulkhead in the front of the trailer and skids should be touching each other, nose to tail.

Obe, riding shotgun, joined me on this, my maiden voyage. He was along because we would have to load and return with some machinery. Following Obe's instructions, I pulled out of the dock in low 2nd and then came to a stop on the level apron. Here he told me to set the trailer's brakes – a chrome handle attached to the steering column – and then climb out to close the trailer doors.

There were no freeways open then requiring us to take U.S. 42 with its undulations and numerous traffic lights. I wasn't complaining, as this gave me a lot of shifting practice. Because the highway was wet, I followed Obe's advice to always gingerly apply the trailer brakes before stepping on the cab brake pedal – this to avoid a jackknife. It was raining even harder on the return trip and loaded with bulky, but light weight machinery (secured with chain and nailed to the wood trailer floor rails), I got another lesson. Starting down a long hill and with no other traffic in sight, Obe told me to slam on the cab brakes just short of locking the wheels and watch the rear view mirror. Cool. The trailer began coming over the center line as if trying to catch the tractor. Releasing the cab brakes brought everything back into line. Now he had me lock up the trailer brakes only. Though not as rapid deceleration when used in tandem with the cab brakes, the rig slowed and stayed in a straight line.

I joined the company full time in 1963 as a salesman. Though we now had an everyday driver he only drove the straight truck, thus if full loads or heavy machinery were involved, I had to double as the semi-driver. By now, the clutch was slipping and the king pins were worn causing a shimmy.

The rig had the standard 5-speed crash box transmission and optional 2-speed electric shift rear axle. Today, every stick-shift transmission includes synchronizers to slow the gears and keep them from grinding during a shift. A crash box has no synchronizers – just cut gears. Thus to keep from grinding (crashing) the gears double-clutching is required. To change up, you have to shift into neutral, let the clutch out to slow the transmission gears down, shove in the clutch and move the shift lever to the higher gear. Down shifting also requires a move to neutral, but while the clutch is out (in neutral) – engine speed must be increased to match the transmission gear speed before again pressing in on the clutch and shifting to the lower gear. Utilizing a tachometer you can make perfect shifts (even without using the clutch!). But, a practiced ear and a "feel" will produce good enough shifts and at a much quicker pace. I had learned to drive a crash box with my first car, a 1952 Crosley which I converted to a fiberglass bodied sports car at age 15 – but that's another story. The '51 International was equipped with the optional 150 gallon, saddle style, diamond-plate fuel tank and west coast mirrors. Power steering was not even an option, but air brakes were standard.

To shift to a higher rear axle ratio, after tripping the switch, entails only letting up on the throttle momentarily - the use of the clutch is not necessary. To shift to the lower rear axle speed while under a load, keep the gas pedal to the metal while quickly disengaging/reengaging the clutch. If not under a load, push the button in while double-clutching into the lower gear. Shifting these old rigs is not so much the mechanics of engine/vehicle speed or the grade of the road as it is based on a feel or sense of when to shift.

Changing transmission gears and axle ratios at the same time is called split shifting and is tricky as it requires all of the above directions to be done at the same time and in a most timely manner. If you try to hurry the axle shift you could end up in "nothing gear" a potential disaster if heading down hill.

I don't know now, and surely didn't know then the load limits of the rig, but I'm certain those limits were greatly exceeded more than once in the years I acted as relief driver. Because inter-plant shipping didn't require weighing loads, how did I know? Most trucks are geared so low and have more torque than horsepower; they can usually start in second gear/hi-range. However, I hauled many loads so heavy that first gear/lo-range (bull-dog low, aka granny gear) was necessary to pull out of an up-hill loading dock. Sometimes, even on level roads, I could not even get into low 5th.

I had also noticed on trips in the '51, the air pressure gauge indicated a higher than normal reading. We worked a trade for a new 1963 Chevrolet tractor. On the '51s final voyage to the Chevrolet dealer, sans the trailer, the air pressure kept building toward the danger zone. As old as the truck was, I was indeed worried that an air line could burst so I drove in the outside lane just in case . . . and in-case happened. Starting down a long hill into the city, I heard the unmistakable sound of an abruptly opened air line. Fighting panic and assuming the brakes had failed, I began edging toward the guard rail while split-shifting from high 5th to low 4th. As the engine screamed, I reached to yank on the emergency brake... .

Flashing through my mind was the Hollywood "in-case" version of oil spray covering the windshield as the truck slammed cars and barriers before upending and bursting into flames. My imaginative thoughts were all for naught. In a few seconds, the "open line" stopped blowing air as I realized there must have been a pressure relief valve that was designed to pop before the air lines did.

Author's 1960 Corvette with collection of trophies

The sun has riz,

and the sun has set,

and we ain't outta Texas yet

The big square trademark radiator filled my outside rearview mirror. He looked like he was going to run over the top of me - and I

144

was running 90 miles per hour! The dark blob in my mirror had been gaining on me for at least the past fifteen minutes. At first I thought it was a cop, but the rate he was closing was steady and not increasing as if it were the police. Besides, 90 was not really considered speeding west of San Antonio. Speed limit signs were seldom encountered and actual "speed limits" in many parts of the west were whatever was "reasonable and proper."

I had left Houston early that morning with limited funds advanced by the Show Winds Theatrical Company. It was early summer, 1961, I was nineteen and had started a dream job as the front man for a live stage show company that produced one-night stands in small towns across the southwest. My first stop-over was Pecos.

I edged closer to the berm and again checked my instruments: Tach, 4000, engine temperature 185°F, oil pressure. . . . It was a huge silver and black Rolls Royce and it was now abreast of me. The mustachioed chauffeur, black cap atop his head, didn't even extend a glance or nod of acknowledgement while the passenger, in the rear seat, couldn't be seen from behind the newspaper he was reading.

This is not happening. This is Texas, USA, and I'm driving the most powerful American made car - the 1960 Corvette! I can't let this go down. For the honor of America, I fed a little more fuel to my three Rochester, two-barrel carburetors and matched the interlopers speed - 110. After a few minutes in his slipstream, I moved over into the east bound lanes and shoved my foot in it. The little roadster responded with push-you-back-in-the-seat acceleration while the twin straight-thru mufflers resonated off the side of the Rolls. I topped out at a little over 125 and then settled back to 120 - a nice easy two-mile-per-minute clip. I gleefully watched the Rolls growing smaller in my mirrors.

It was hot, maybe 90 or so, and even the rush of air at such a high speed didn't help much. My cheerfulness quickly faded upon glancing at my gauges. The engine temperature was approaching 220 degrees! I had removed the thermostat prior to beginning the trip knowing the little 283 engine would need all the advantages it could get in the hot south-west summer. The engine was basically the 270 horsepower version to which I had exchanged the two-four barrel carbs for three-duces on straight linkage. The reason was for better

145

response during high speed cornering and improved fuel economy - it got 14.5 MPG at a cruising speed of 90 per. Other attributes included metallic brake linings, quick steering, 4-speed transmission, heavy duty shocks and a 3.70 rear axle.

I had been running all day at 90 without straining the engine, but the extra 30 MPH had been too much. I cut back down to 90. Sure enough, 15 minutes later here came the Rolls with the haughty chauffeur and oblivious passenger - 110, steady as she goes. Well, we don't have to tell anyone - obviously they won't - they didn't even know they had slighted an American icon.

Hot, dirty, tired and coming down with a cold, I stopped at a Pecos hospital where I conned the resident into giving me a shot of penicillin. Then twelve hours in an air conditioned cabin at Jim Bob & Mary Beth's Tourist Haven and I was ready to begin work. The agreement was; I was to deliver and post bills in common places of the city. I was also to visit any and all local radio stations and newspapers with publicity releases and offer interviews. Posting the flyers was without incident. However, the radio stations and the only local newspaper were reluctant to give me an interview or a promise to plug the upcoming show – seems they had heard my company's song before.

I was allowed two days to complete my work before moving on to the next municipality. At each town the Company was to have waiting for me a money order, care of general delivery. On the morning of the third day there was still no letter at the post office. I called Houston and was told some long tale that I should not worry they'll make it up to me in Farmington, New Mexico, the next scheduled stop. Boy was I naive. They didn't send me out completely without support. They gave me $30.00 for gas money, which, at .20/gallon was good for about 800 miles.

Around noon the next day, I rolled into Roswell just as a local parade was mustering on the main drag. Hand waving to the crowds like I was one of the floats, got into line behind what turned out to be the mayor's car - a '61 Chevy Convertible. About the time the parade got to the center of town, a motorcycle cop pulled alongside of me, signaling that I should follow him. Oops. At the police station, I tried to tell them I was just following traffic when I somehow got mixed up with the parade vehicles. That was almost truthful inasmuch as a cop, way back at the beginning, asked me if I was in the parade and I nodded yes. Since they couldn't get the mayor to forgo his parade and ceremonial affair to hear my case, the sergeant ordered that I be escorted out of town. Sometimes ya get lucky. Now I was on my way to Route 66 and Albuquerque for dinner and a night's sleep.

The next day, I gassed up and inquired of the best route to Farmington. The locals at the gas station, while admiring my car and asking if I was on the Route 66 TV show advised, I should stay on 66 to Gallup and then turn north as the roads running out of Albuquerque to the four-corners area were not all paved. I didn't tell them I was on the show, but I didn't tell them I wasn't, either. On my way out of town, I noticed I had picked up a few followers - kids from the gas station who had tried to goad me into a race. The leader of the pack - driving a maroon 1957 Chevrolet with louvers on the hood, lowering blocks and a shaved nose and deck - kept riding up on my rear bumper. Once or twice, when traffic permitted, he pulled alongside, shoved it into second gear and goosed it a few times while his shotgun called for a race. After a few miles of this, the taunts and threats became abusive and it was clear I needed to do something.

Picking a stretch of Highway 66 that looked to have a sharp curve with a clear view at the end of a short straightaway, I changed down into third and opened the throttle full. The '57, taken by surprise, lagged a hundred feet back by the time I had entered the hard right hand turn. One of the other attributes I added to my Vette was a panel that included switches for my brake lights, tail lights, left tail light, four-way-flasher (not a factory option yet) and under-hood lights. The tail light switch was in case I was being followed, at night, by someone I didn't want to catch me - such as a cop. I could turn out the tail lights making it very hard for him to see me. The left tail light switch was for the same purpose, whereas if a cop was chasing a car with two tail lights, but after a few hills and dales, the only car in front of him had one tail light, he would think the car he was chasing had turned off. It worked exactly as expected, but that's another story.

Hurtling down the highway at close to 90, and with the '57 coming on strong, things got very busy. Just before trouncing the binders, I flipped the switch cancelling the brake lights. With a quick heal-toe maneuver I jammed the shift lever into second gear redlining the engine. The car shuttered as the speed dropped. Tires howling in protest, I induced an under-steer setting up a four wheel drift. As the right front tire, just over the edge of the pavement and on the dirt berm fought for adhesion, and just before the apex, I poured the coal to her while straightening the wheel to compensate for drift. Once clear of the corner, I stole a glance at my rear view mirror. The Chevy driver, obviously thinking that if I could take the corner without braking, he could too - learned to late something wasn't right. I couldn't see exactly what happened, but there was a lot of dust and I never saw them again.

Farmington was void of any hotels or motels, but I did find a nice home that offered rooms to rent - $3.00 per night including breakfast and dinner. That was after I checked the post office - no mail here either. I couldn't help being an optimist; my mother was a Pollyanna. I began the next day calling on the local radio station. Here, a kindly, older DJ/station manager took pity on me and told me how, after the town had been excited about and helped promote the theatrical company's promise to come last year - never showed up. When I told him that I hadn't been paid he offered to treat me to dinner at his lodge in Durango, Colorado.

The trip through the mountains to this old west town, nestled down into a valley amid jagged mountain peaks, was the most beautiful scenery I had ever seen. The "one dog" town was right out of a Louis L'Amour dime novel as was the rustic Moose Lodge, complete with hand hewn, exposed rafters and, of course, a giant, moose head mounted over a huge stone fireplace. The western attired members, in their scuffed boots and sweat-stained hats, were authentic - not fancy fringed-shirted Hollywood cowboy wannabees.

Arriving back in Farmington, I found a parking ticket on my windshield. It seemed that everywhere I went, cops were attracted to my Corvette. Not, I'm sure, as enthusiasts, but because they assumed sooner or later the driver was going to race, speed, spin his tires, make noise or all of the above. Their concerns were not without merit. The $1.00 ticket could become $100.00 if not paid within 24 hours. Twenty-four or a thousand hours, I wasn't about to pay it. It wasn't the principle of the thing, I just didn't have the dollar to spare. Besides, it would be more fun to try to beat 'em out of it.

148

Early the next morning, I headed for the post office. That was, of course, after I paid my room bill and had a full breakfast. The matronly, middle aged, everybody's-mom-lady-of-the-house, in her gingham dress, wished me good luck. The postmaster told me the mail truck wasn't due for about an hour. I walked to the corner drug store, ordered a coke at the soda fountain and read a three-day old copy of the local paper.

The mail contained nothing for me. Then it was back to the drug store where I used the pay phone to place a collect call to the producer. He refused my call! Well, at least I got gas money to get this far. California here I come.

Just before noon, and as I hit the town's western limit, the red light on the '59 Ford police car that had been following me came on. I stopped, got out and walked back to the cruiser.

"You gonna pay that ticket, boy," the rotund, red faced cop spat.

"Not right now, sir. But I will."

"Looks to me like you're leaving town - and that's another crime iffins you gotta outstanding ticket."

"Uh, no sir. I was just going to run a mile or two on the highway. My plugs were beginning to foul from all that town driving I'd been doing and I thought I'd blow 'em out a little. I can't leave until I do the radio interview tonight," I lied.

"Well, go ahead, but if you ain't back in ten minutes, I'm gonna radio to Shiprock to stop you and lock you up. Ya hear?"

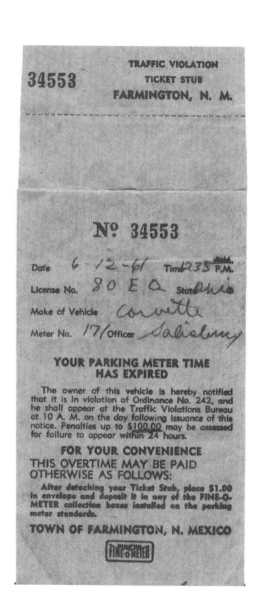

TRAFFIC VIOLATION
TICKET STUB
FARMINGTON, N. M.

34553

N? 34553

Date 6-12-61 Time 235 P.M.
License No. 80 E Q State Ohio
Make of Vehicle Corvette
Meter No. 17 Officer Salisbury

**YOUR PARKING METER TIME
HAS EXPIRED**

The owner of this vehicle is hereby notified
that it is in violation of Ordinance No. 242, and
he shall appear at the Traffic Violations Bureau
at 10 A. M. on the day following issuance of this
notice. Penalties up to $100.00 may be assessed
for failure to appear within 24 hours.

FOR YOUR CONVENIENCE
THIS OVERTIME MAY BE PAID
OTHERWISE AS FOLLOWS:

After detaching your Ticket Stub, place $1.00
in envelope and deposit it in any of the FINE-O-
METER collection boxes installed on the parking
meter standards.

TOWN OF FARMINGTON, N. MEXICO

The Ticket

It was 25 miles to Shiprock and then another 25 to the Arizona
border. Approaching the turn-off to this final town, at my normal
4000 RPM cruising speed of 90 MPH, I could see two police cars,

150

lights flashing, on the right shoulder. A uniformed officer was standing in the middle of the road, his hand held up, palm forward. I slowed to about 35, shifted to 2nd to wait for an on-coming pickup truck to clear the road block. With the left lane now open, I moved across the double yellow line as the officers began waving their hands and shouting. I had to put two wheels on the dirt shoulder to keep from hitting them as they watched, dumbfounded, America's only real sports car rocket away from them. It was a gamble, but I figured the chances of another cop being between me and the border to be slim.

I'd never experienced 106°F - and neither had my Vette! Arizona - hot, dusty and hotter. At those daytime temperatures, I couldn't hold much over 55 and the air blowing on my feet from the cowl vent was so scorching I had to close it. Gripping the steering wheel caused my hands to sweat, but sticking them out of the window to dry, burned. Back on Route 66 at my first gas stop, I learned most cross country drivers only drove at night - when the desert cooled the air. Long before Flagstaff, I found a rarity, an air conditioned restaurant, and hunkered down till evening. Because everyone traveled at night, the traffic was the most I'd seen since leaving Houston.

Somewhere in the early morning hours I started down the mountains from Barstow into the San Bernardino valley. The temperature plunged so much I had to stop to paper my radiator with a road map so the engine could generate enough heat to warm the interior of the cockpit.

Southern California in the early 60s was cool cars, perfect weather, sun-tanned bodies – and everything they've said about it. However, I was scheduled to begin college in the fall and I still wanted to see the northern states. So, after a two week visit with my mother's family, I was eastbound.

My road atlas showed a small town at about the limit of my fuel range. I planned to gas up there and spend the night. Arriving around midnight, I was dismayed to find no motel and the little burg closed up tight - including the only gas station. A map check revealed the next town was about 75 miles further east. It was a beautiful full moon night and since I'd been climbing for the past few hours, I was sure I was now on the downside of the Rockies. Not having passed a car – in either direction – for quite some time, I took to killing the engine, turning off the headlights and coasting down long mountain passages to save fuel. The exhilarating moon-lit roll worked as I just made it to my destination with the gas gauge showing below empty.

The author's father, at age 93, and after reading this story, told the following about his trip from Cincinnati to Los Angeles in 1928.

"The first thing we did was purchase a rear view mirror and water pump because those items didn't come with the Model 'T' Ford. The parts were readily available at a Leo's, Checkers or Western Auto stores for a dollar or two. Soon after installing our travel necessities on our used 1927 Ford roadster, my friend, Phil, and I, both nineteen years of age, headed west. For this adventure, I took vacation time from my job as a draftsman/pattern maker for the Nivison-Weiskopf company in Reading, Ohio.

"We drove to Indianapolis, then through St. Louis, Kansas City, Denver and Salt Lake City. The main road, U.S. 40, was very rough in spots, had minimal gas stations and questionable drinking water. We slung a canvas bag filled with potable water across the hood of the car. The trip was never without adventure with numerous flat tires, other breakdowns and at more than one point, we, along with other travelers, had to ford rivers and streams! Upon entering the Utah desert we stopped to pick up a hitch-hiker - a young man about our age who was trying to get to California where he had been promised a job with the Associated Press. He vowed to send us a press card as soon as he was established - it never arrived.

"Crossing the desert at night I was the first to become drowsy. Phil was driving, the hitch-hiker in the middle and I was next to the passenger door. Because of the remoteness of the roads in these sparsely populated, open plains and mountainous regions of this vast continent, we carried a pearl-handled .25 caliber pistol for protection. There were three of us now, and thinking nothing of it, I turned the handgun over to the stranger to act as guard while I napped and Phil continued driving.

"The hitch-hiker was with us for at least one night and two days as we wound our way south to Flagstaff, Arizona where we found U.S.

Route 66 - in its first year of dedication. In Barstow, California the hitch-hiker left us as he was headed north to San Francisco. Phil and I continued on to Los Angeles."

Author's Note: Early transcontinental routes were void of speed limits and included miles of unpaved roadway, single lane bridges - or no bridges at all - and few signs or markers. The original Route 66 ran 2400 miles through eight states from Chicago to Santa Monica. This federally designated highway was immortalized by John Steinbeck's, "The Grapes of Wrath," Dorthea Lang's dust bowl photographs, the 60s TV show, "Route 66," and countless travelers such as the author and his father.

MOVING ON

1960 Corvette

Seeing her at her Mother's funeral forced memories
Forever melded to the sentimental portions of my mind.

In my 13th year, the summer of 1954, the Miller's moved next door. I was just starting to notice girls and Barbara – Barbie - got my attention when she beat me at a game of mumbly-peg. And, even though she was a tom-boy, she was a very good looking tom-boy. Nothing was ever said, but my best friend, Carl, knew that the looks between her cyan and my hazel eyes meant a destiny that didn't include him. Our families became close in many ways. Barbie and I

154

were the same age, her brother and I swam on the school team together and our mothers became the very best of friends.

Throughout high school, I was on the wild side - a hot rodder - and only dated "chicks." I was embarrassed to call Barbie until I'd sowed my oats. I re-noticed her when she came over to swim late in the summer of '61. Now, I was enrolled in college and more mature - and she was so pretty. Somehow I talked her into a date for that Saturday night. I then spent an entire day cleaning and polishing my 1960 Corvette. The Vette was rigged for road racing with the quick-steering adapter, HD shocks, metallic brake linings and 3" x 6" galvanized pipe welded to the exhaust header pipes. The only external change to the car was the addition of Marchal head lamps to replace the outboard standard sealed beam lights.

Temperature wise, it was a perfect Cincinnati evening and I had the top off and soft music playing on the RCA 45 record player I had installed on the "chicken bar" ('cuz the radio was all static due to the solid spark plug wires). She wore something white and was so pretty – wait, I already said that. Slowly, so as to enjoy the music and not disturb her with the loud exhaust, we motored to Sorrento's restaurant, turning every head we passed. Though Corvettes weren't common and car aficionados would always look, everyone noticed a beautiful blonde.

We spent a lot of time together that late summer – swimming, dancing, movies and other fun stuff. One warm night, while watching an Elvis Presley movie at the drive-in, The King sang "Can't Help Falling In Love." At the line, "Take my hand, take my whole life too… ." we instinctively reached to hold hands. I don't remember the song being "our song," but whenever I've heard it, I've thought of Barbie. The end of September found her returning to the University of Colorado at Boulder and our courtship continued via mail.

In mid January, exams over and during a conversation with my friend and fellow hot rod club member, Kookie, I suggested we run out to Boulder. He didn't have anything else going on and was game, especially after I promised Barbie would fix him up with a real honey.

We picked up U.S. 36 in downtown Indianapolis, a reprieve, after following mostly state highways with their inherent undulations, stream-chasing routes and long, wild grasses growing over the edge of the pavement (expressways yet to open). West of the city the traffic thinned out and we were able to return to our cruising speed of 90 MPH. The Corvette had three Rochester 2-barrel carburetors on straight linkage and at that speed the engine was running 4000 RPM which was well into the power curve of the Duntov cam. In other words, it was a comfortable clip that produced over 14 miles per gallon.

Somewhere around 5:00 a.m., in a dense fog, a wheel came off. Kookie was driving and did a great job of keeping the Vette on the road. There was no damage to the car, but, due to the thick fog we never found the tire and wheel. We took a lug nut from each of the other wheels and used those three nuts to hold the spare tire on. Limping into the next town we found a Chevrolet dealer and after a two hour wait for them to open, we were on our way again.

Deep into western Kansas, running the usual 90 per, a semi-truck emerged about a half mile ahead. It appeared we would pass the truck, maintaining the present rate, in the middle of an intersection. The land was flat and the cross road was clear, so I just held her steady at 4000 RPM. Halfway around the semi and over the double yellow line, I was startled to see a state trooper on the truck's front bumper! The noise from the muffler by-pass reverberating off the truck was deafening and produced a look of surprised outrage on the trooper's face as we roared past. Not for an instant did I think I could talk my way out of speeding, excessive noise, driving left of center and passing in an intersection.

I went to full throttle while Kookie scanned the map. One Hundred . . . a hundred and ten . . . two-miles-per-minute. We were a lightning bolt on wheels. My co-pilot leaned over and shouted that there was only one little town and then about ten miles to Colorado. We had to chance that there weren't any other cops between us and the border. Now my attention was riveted to controlling this 300 horse-powered, plastic-bodied roadster – a land-rocket that was sans power brakes, power steering or steel-belted-radial-tires. At these speeds even glancing at the gauges was forsaken. I had to rely on engine sounds, the feel of the wheel, gut instincts and luck. Billboards and highway signs such as Burma-Shave and Mail Pouch became mere peripheral splashes of color.

156

Coming into the small burg, a pandemonium of smoke and danger - fire shooting from the open lake-pipes - people stopped and stared, mouths agape. I forced the Vette to just under 60 in second gear to negotiate a hard left turn then got a piece of third before having to shut down for a tight chicane in the heart of town. Once through the business district, I red-lined in third gear before leveling off again at 90. The state trooper was nowhere in sight.

Inside Colorado, with Denver in view, we came around a bend in the road and there sat two highway patrol cars. Both pulled out after us. We got out of their sight over a small hill and slammed to a stop. Having anticipated this from previous high speed runs, Kookie and I were both wearing like-colored shirts. When the officers finally pulled up behind us, we were standing outside the car studying a road map. They couldn't give us a ticket, because they were unable to determine who was driving. However, they let us know that Kansas had called that we were coming and they were going to follow us all the way through their state if necessary. They stayed with us until we turned off at Boulder.

At the university, we found a motel and called Barbie. She came right over and the hug and kiss made it all worthwhile. We got a little shut-eye, Barbie came through with a co-ed for Kookie and we did the college scene. The next day, Kookie wanted to see a mountain and the girls found the way where we took pictures and enjoyed the day.

The home-bound leg was uneventful except for the final stretch in Indiana . . . where on lazy, sunny, summer days giant deciduous trees over-hang the country roadways, their branches reaching out as if to shake hands. Uneventful: except this was night, the dead of winter and we picked up a cop. I quickly tripped the switch I had installed to cancel the left tail light. A few miles further down this highway that snaked in and out of those towering trees, the officer who had been chasing two tail lights, now only saw a vehicle with one light and surely figured we turned at a side road – which he must have done as we never saw him again.

The trip out, due to losing the tire, took almost 24 hours. Coming back, we covered the 1190 miles in 19 hours five minutes, including fuel stops - a 63 MPH average. All of this on two lane roads, with no side-lines, very narrow, if any, shoulders and through downtown

Indianapolis and every other city, town and burg. I've never been sure the trip wasn't more about the opportunity to road race than it was to see my girl.

I developed some very strong feelings for her and I know she pined for me also, but the timing wasn't right. Both of us had agendas - places to go, things to do, worlds to conquer and commitments were a long way off.

It is said that everyone experiences three loves:

The one they marry;

The one they're glad they didn't marry;
and the one that got away.

Barbie and I kept in touch, but with careers and dating others the touch got lighter. Within a few years, Barbara accepted a job in California and . . . married. Me? As soon as I figured out that it was just as much fun to be the chaser as it was the chasee, I became a police officer.

The Corvette? A few months after the Colorado trip, before I burned the valves experimenting with nitro-methane and sold it to an unsuspecting dealer, I made one last run. They had just opened the six-lane Interstate between Cincinnati and Dayton and nine of us, all in Corvettes - three rows of three - broke in the new road. With seven Vettes to block cops, two at a time would line up, and from a roll, run flat out. I was up against a '59 270 with a higher rear axle ratio. I beat him from 70 to about 130, and then he came on by.

Yeah, I know, we were crazy back then. But traffic was light, cops fewer, radar not perfected and we were very lucky. Lucky to survive and lucky to have lived during that era.

Late in the spring of 1996, and now a widower, my second wife, Annette, and I were honored to be treated to lunch with Mrs. Miller and my mother. Barbie, who has known Annette since grade school, was in town for a visit and also joined us. Both of my wives have known about "Barbie and me." I made certain they did - a tinge of jealousy never hurt any relationship. I always wondered if Barbara, in the same vein, kept Larry on his toes, too.

Never being able to satiate aspirations;
Is better than not having

Any fantasies at all.

At some point during the luncheon, Barbie and I found ourselves alone . . . and 42 years since our eyes locked in that game of mumbly-peg, I asked this girl next door, "Did life turn out okay? Are you happy?" She smiled, her blue eyes twinkling, "Oh yes. Surely you remember your mother always telling us, 'the secret to life is the ability to adapt to change.' And you?"

I smiled out of the corner of my mouth and gave her a slow wink, "Can't argue with my mom."

After the funeral Barbara introduced me to her daughters,

one of which immediately turned to her sisters and whispered,

"He's Klein. He could have been our father."

Cessna 172

The plan was for the three of us to drive Steve's new '66 Chevrolet station wagon, loaded with hunting gear, from Cincinnati to a remote county in South Carolina for a Canada Goose hunt. Our high spirits diminished as we got stuck behind logging trucks, farm wagons and small town traffic even before leaving Ohio. We soon realized our ETA was going to be so late as to cut into our hunt time. A new strategy emerged to charter a plane for the balance of the trip and, lo and behold, there appeared just outside of Huntington, West Virginia, a momentous omen in the form of a sign: Airport 5 miles. All of us, mid-20s junior executives, prided ourselves on being able to make sound and quick decisions. Upon arrival at this single runway airport we quickly located an open sided shed – they probably called it a hanger. Leaning against the only partially sided side was a little lean-to with a placard displaying the magic words: Charter Service.

None of us had even been in a small plane before, but that was a fact nobody wanted to admit. Steve and I had flown commercial, but Craig, the third member of the hunting party, had never been higher than three beers. Steve was the kind of guy who was used to taking charge just because he was bigger than most and had a strong commanding voice. He also could be very verbally abusive when upset. Craig and I were more passive inasmuch as we tended to wait out aggression before taking action.

The manager, upon our acceptance of the cost of the plane and a pilot for two nights and the return flight, introduced us to our air-chauffer, Hap. Hap was about middle age, rotund, a most jovial type, and confident of his flying abilities. Being eager to go, we quickly loaded our stuff – crammed is a better word – into the cargo hold of a 4-place, single engine Cessna. You could see the airframe flex and the tires compress as each of us took turns climbing in. I won the coin toss and elected to fly in the co-pilot's seat. Here we go.

Hap, after showing us his pilot's license, told the manager he'd file a flight plan via radio once in the air and in route. Taxiing to the runway, our pilot mentioned we seemed a mite hefty, but he was convinced he could get us airborne. Steve was at least two-ten, Craig one-eighty-five and I was the lightweight at one-sixty-five. Add the duffle bags, boots, winter coats, guns and ammo plus Hap and his luggage and heavy-my-kitty comes to mind.

Turning onto the runway, Hap asked for permission to take off as he opened the throttle. About half way down this mountaintop runway a red light flashed on the instrument panel along with a buzzing sound. I pointed to the light and looked at Hap, who smiled, saying it was just a stall warning light and pay no attention. What did I know?

The pilot did look a bit tense, but the plane made it into the air, clearing the trees at the extreme end of the runway by at least 10 feet. If he was tense, I was scared stiff. The guys in the back seats, who had no knowledge of the warning light or couldn't see the looming trees or end of the runway, were gazing out the window enjoying their first private plane flight.

The sky was heavy with clouds and rain squalls could be seen in many directions. These conditions produced turbulence that rocked and tossed us and the plane around. Hap soon stated that if we could get above the clouds it would be a much smoother ride. But because the plane didn't have radar, he continued to explain, he was not allowed to fly through the clouds. However, within a few minutes, he spotted a hole in this ominous overcast. As he started a slow spiral into the hole, he grabbed the microphone and began transmitting, first by identifying the aircraft and then continued to ask permission to fly through this break in the cloud cover. Of course, as with all two-way radios, when one is broadcasting (holding the mic button to talk) no one can cut in or talk to you. Hap, instead of releasing the transmit button to allow for acknowledgment and permission to fly through the break in the clouds continued to broadcast. In order to comply with flight regulations he began filing his flight plan – where he was headed, where from and a general flight path. What happened next was probably the scariest event I've ever witnessed without actually witnessing anything tangible.

Hap began his transmission: "This is Cessna Two-seven Tango out of Huntington. We are at 4700 feet and climbing, 3-miles southwest of radio station tower WXXZ, requesting permission to go through a hole in the clouds. Our destination is… ."

As the plane ascended into the solid cloud bank, I could see the radio tower he was referring to and I could see the altimeter slowing passing the 4700, then 4800 foot markers. Those reading were probably plus or minus at least 50 feet as Hap had not received a barometer reading as yet.

After about a minute or so of transmitting and circling upward, Hap released the mic switch – at which time the air controller immediately came on, and in a clear and loud voice said:

"CESSNA TWO-SEVEN TANGO, PERMISSION DENIED, DIVE IMMEDIATELY. REPEAT DIVE IMMEDIATELY. PIEDMONT AIRLINES COMING THROUGH THE CLOUDS AT 5000 FEET, THREE MILES SOUTHWEST OF RADIO STATION TOWER WXXZ. DIVE, DIVE DIVE"

Fortunately, Hap wasn't the type of guy you had to tell twice. Instantly, he rolled the plane over and into what seemed to me as a death spiral. My last look at the altimeter showed 4950.

Stomachs settled, we eventually found another hole, received permission and flew the rest of the way in bright sunshine. We never did see the Piedmont airliner, but I'm sure he saw us on his radar.

The homebound leg was not quite as exciting even though we fought turbulence most of the way. An hour out of Huntington, my rear seat passenger, Craig, complained that he was air sick and was going to toss his cookies and if I didn't give him something to barf in he was going to retch all over Steve, who was sitting directly in front of him in the co-pilot's seat. Steve, using a string of profanities and references to my legitimacy, turned and hollered to me to give Craig something to puke in and to do it now. I reached behind into the cargo area where, after fumbling around between sets of boots, I was able to pull the exact one I sought - an only-worn-once L.L. Bean leather beauty. Craig immediately grabbed the tendered footgear and heaved. Because plane windows don't open, I covered my nose with my shirt sleeve while trying to stifle my laughter. Steve, who now began complaining about the odor demanded to know what was so damn funny. When he calmed down and I couldn't contain myself any longer, I said, "It's your boot!"

The hunt? Zero. Not only did none of us bag a goose, but we never even saw one close enough to get a shot off .

A BADGE, A GUN AND SOME FUN

Patrolman Badge and Duty Revolver

ARMED ROBBERY I

"Attention all cars, all departments, armed robbery just occurred, The First National Bank, Kemper and Hilborne, Springdale, Ohio, wanted are two male blacks, armed with a silver revolver, last seen on foot east bound from the bank's parking lot. Car 8-3-8 the North West quadrant. Car 4-6-8 the South West quadrant. Car 4-1-7... ." Springdale, a suburb just north of us, would respond to the scene, while the county dispatcher assigned beat cars from other suburbs and the sheriff's office to take posts in a quadrant surrounding the area of most probable escape.

Swell. On a beautiful summer morning working my first day shift in months and I've got to find a suitable location where unknown robbers in a non-descript vehicle might be headed my way. Waiting for others to clear their calls, I keyed the mic, "Four-six-eight" okay.

I was, for all intents and purposes working alone, the Chief being the only other Woodlawn officer on duty in our small suburban village, just north of Cincinnati. Our head LEO, who always worked the day shift, was dressed in a business suit for the usual meetings and other diplomatic stuff Chiefs have to do.

In my marked patrol car and heading north on Route 4, I looked at every car coming south. The morning traffic was light and I eyeballed a lone car coming at me - with only one occupant, a male black. The driver looked hard at me and then studied his inside mirror as he passed. Humm. Watching my outside mirror, I used my left foot to lightly apply the brakes to see his reaction. A head popped up! Whoa. One dude hiding in the backseat?

Tripping the roof lights, activating the siren, keying the mic, turning the big, almost new,'72 police packaged Plymouth around on a narrow 4-laner without hitting anyone and then going to full throttle can make modern-day multi-taskers seem like children playing dodge-ball.

"Four-six-eight, I'm in pursuit, black over tan late model Chevrolet, southbound Route 4 approaching one-twenty-six. Possible vehicle reference earlier armed robbery broadcast."

They had about a half mile lead on me, but the opened 4-barrled V8 rocketed to over 100 mph in seconds. What light traffic there was pulled over to give me room as I closed the distance.

Our patrol cars were the very apt1972 Plymouth Fury Pursuit with the Special Handling package that included heavy-duty: front & rear sway bars, torsion bars, rear leaf springs and shocks. The 15"x6.5JJ wheels had high-performance tires mounted to them and semi-metallic front disc brakes, with 11" x 2 ½ rear brakes for stopping. Other police package attributes consisted of maximum cooling package, dual spotlights, 60 amp alternator and the 400 CID engine with 4-bbl carb. The speedometer was certified and calibrated to 140 mph. Because the mayor felt it was intimidating, there was no cage or other separation between the front and back bench seats and our 12 gauge shotgun was kept in the trunk.

In operation 24/7 and piloted by a dozen different officers, these scout cars took a beating seldom lasting more than a year.

Added by our department was twin rotating red lights, siren and alley lights on a roof bar. On the inside, we had the interior dome light rigged so it wouldn't shine when opening the door, plus we had the controls for the roof lights and sirens mounted to a custom panel on the underside of the dash.

"All cars stand-by. Four-six-eight in pursuit. 4-6-8 is this vehicle wanted?"

Facing a double line of cars stopped for the light at State Route 126, I got a glimpse of the black/tan entering a service station at the corner; drive through the lot and onto Route 126, avoiding the traffic light – a violation of law.

"4-6-8 affirmative. Subject vehicle is now eastbound 126 from Route 4."

Red lights flashing, siren yelping, I crossed over the double yellow line as on-coming cars slammed on brakes, pulled right, left – any-which-way to avoid me. Slowing to maybe 40 or 50 at the intersection, I caught a little gravel causing a fishtail going to full throttle as I straightened out for the east bound highway. The whooshing of the four-barrel carb sucking air was distinct even over the siren.

I was aware of radio traffic of other cars responding, but my full concentration was on tracking – catching the black/tan. I'd lost sight of them approaching Wayne Avenue. Hoping Evendale's 4-1-7 would be coming west on 126, I turned south onto Wayne hurtling airborne over a slight hump in the roadway. About a mile down, as I blew past a residential driveway, I caught sight of the Chevrolet. Slamming on the binders, jamming the scout car in reverse, I searched for a house number - and the robbers with the gun! Were they waiting for me?

I fumbled for the mic: "Four-six-eight the vehicle is stopped in the 600 block of Wayne. 2-7."

"Two-seven 4-6-8. 4-1-7?"

Out of the corner of my eye I saw one subject running away from the Chevy. I pulled in behind the car that was between two houses and facing a wooded area. Fully aware that at least one desperate man could be hiding behind the buildings, the vehicle, or in the woods - waiting to use the silver handgun or whatever else they might be armed with to ambush me. I didn't - couldn't hesitate. Service revolver in hand, I approached the black over tan get-away car.

The author, 1972, Woodlawn, OH P.D.

Nothing. Nobody. No sound, save the sirens of my backup still a mile or so away. I ran to the woods – the point the fugitive was last seen – but the foliage was too great to see more than ten yards or so. I stopped and held my breath, no sign or sound of anyone on foot. As portable or personal radios were not yet standard equipment, I headed back to the scene to call in on the radio for additional units and a dog if available.

With help from 4-1-7, we did a cursory search of the Chevy finding a shirt and a chrome plated revolver. Within a few more minutes, a patrol car from another neighboring community, Lincoln Heights, approached with a shirtless, male black in tow. It was a Bingo moment as I recognized the punk in his custody as the driver of the car that passed me on Route 4.

The shirtless dude froze as the Evendale officer drew his revolver and ordered the 17 year old kid to slowly turn around and place both hands on the roof of the patrol car. Wide-eyed, he stammered, "Are you going to shoot me?"

Four-one-seven, calmly replied, "Naw, not today. We're only allowed to shoot on Tuesdays and this is Wednesday, isn't it?"

The Lincoln Heights officer dead-panned, "Officer, today is Tuesday." The kid's jaw dropped as 4-1-7 raised his gun. . .smiled and said, I don't feel like it, get in the back of the cruiser. Tension broken, we all had a good laugh – well, all except the 17 year old.

With the money and gun recovered, we waited for a Springdale unit to bring a witness to the scene. The kid was identified as the robber by the bank teller and was the turned over to Springdale for transportation to their lockup. The rest of us went back on patrol as we were the only uniformed LEOs on duty in our respective communities.

Small suburban communities must work together and back each other up as the cost of large forces is prohibitive. The late 60s and early 70s were heady times; America was under-going tumultuous introspection. The baby-boomer generation was coming of age and were distancing themselves from their parents' world of dress codes, verboten drugs, politics-as-usual and behind-closed-door sex. In addition, some of the black population of this peer group was impatient with civil rights won in court battles and thus prepped themselves for violent uprisings. Police "riot" tactics consisted of billy-clubs, chemical Mace, tear gas, fire hoses, 12 gauge pump

168

shotguns and 6-shot revolvers. SWAT teams had only been recently formed in the larger cities and counties.

One of my most memorable backups to Lincoln Heights was to respond to a call of their station being under attack. Upon arrival, myself and another Woodlawn officer planted ourselves at the perimeter of a riotous crowd that was throwing rocks and bottles at the police station. As more units from other surrounding agencies arrived, the rioters, about 50 men, women and teens, turned their attention to us. A rock struck the grips of my holstered service revolver taking a chip of wood. I retrieved the riot gun from the trunk and stood ready – for what I really didn't know. The show of force soon caused the rioters to disperse.

The 17 year-old robbery perp ratted out his accomplice and both eventually copped pleas for a ten year suspended sentence – this being their first felony.

In an average year over 150 police officers are killed in the line of duty – some even by punks younger than 17. You never think about it while it happens, but after arresting any felon, especially when guns are involved, the sweat and shakes usually come-on an hour or so after it's all over. On the upside, it's a lot of fun.

ARMED ROBBERY II

It started out quiet enough for a Friday when my partner, John Campbell, and I began our Midnight to eight tour of duty. I was four-six-eight, the first-responder car, and John, the senior officer was car 4-6-9, the backup. We're police officers, our bailiwick is a small village adjacent to Cincinnati. Being a pint-sized community, we don't have the luxury of having our own dispatcher and thus rely on the County for all radio messages as did thirty-three other like towns and villages on the network. With this much radio traffic going through one dispatcher on one channel, all transmissions were on a very professional level with superfluous talk almost non-existent. To talk to another car or give detailed information to the dispatcher, the officers were to use the telephone, or if that was not practical, radio channel two could be used - but only with the dispatcher's permission.

The early part of the shift was consumed by checking the business areas and watching for drunk drivers with very little radio traffic, for us. The rest of the county was having a regular Friday night with many calls for bar fights, domestic trouble, and an occasional burglary report. About 2:00 AM, our quiet night became history as the dispatcher put out an all-county broadcast with run-together-words and sentences only cops can decipher.

"Attention all cars all departments armed robbery just occurred the King Kwik Market Route 4 and Connersville Road Fairfield wanted are three black male subjects wearing ski masks and armed with a sawed-off shotgun and blue steel revolver last seen south bound State Route 4 in an older model Chrysler sedan black-over-white in color, bearing Ohio six five three Charles David."

State Route 4 ran through the middle of our beat, and even though Fairfield was ten miles and one county north, I positioned myself at our northern boundary. After half an hour of waiting, I moved on, assuming the get-away car wasn't coming my way.

Soon the Dispatcher radioed our department to advise that the subject license was registered to a William Pilder of 11457 Shelter Road. That address was in our village and in a basically decent neighborhood. The Pilder family was not known as a harbor for criminals or trouble makers. Perhaps the person who copied the license number got it wrong – as often happens under stress.

My partner radioed that since he was near the location, he'd check it out. I didn't hear anymore and when 4-6-9 and I met a little later he indicated the Pilder place was a dark house on an empty driveway.

Back out on patrol I watched an older model black-over-white sedan approach me from the opposite direction on SR 4. I caught a glimpse of the license plate as we passed - it matched the one from the earlier broadcast and there were three occupants in the vehicle. As I started to turn my police-packaged Plymouth around, they took off at a high rate of speed. Fumbling, fighting, wrestling with the gear shift, steering wheel and emergency light/siren switch, I did my best to begin pursuit while keying the microphone:

"4-6-8 emergency traffic."

"All cars stand-by. 4-6-8, your emergency traffic."

"4-6-8 I'm in pursuit, black over white, Chrysler sedan bearing Ohio six, five, three, Charles David. We're south bound Route Four approaching Snyder Road. They've killed their lights"

"Okay 4-6-8. Four-six-eight are you aware these subjects possibly wanted armed robbery reference earlier broadcast?"

"4-6-8 affirmative. They're now running over 80."

In operation 24/7 and piloted by a dozen different officers, these 1972 Plymouth Police-packaged, scout cars took a beating and seldom lasted more than a year.

"4-6-9, 4-1-7, 4-3-2, Four-six-eight in pursuit black over white Chrysler sedan south bound Route Four at Snyder. Subject vehicle believed wanted reference earlier broadcast for armed robbery. Be advised subject vehicle has no headlights."

The Plymouth was barely keeping up with the perp's. Under normal conditions the Fury would have caught them, but because we were a suburban community with zero miles of open highway, the patrol cars did a lot of idling and low speed cruising. Thus, within a couple of thousand miles after a tune-up the engines would begin to develop a miss.

I darted my eyes to the calibrated speedometer – 95! Then suddenly they slammed on their brakes and turned onto Rickman - a dead end residential street in a heavily wooded area.

"4-6-8 they just turned west on Rickman"

I assumed the dispatcher and other cars heard me and were responding, but I was now totally focused on the Chrysler as it crested a small hill. Unexpectedly, the black over white slowed to a stop. The interior light briefly lit. The significance of this didn't register, though I slowed thinking perhaps they were going to run into the woods or make a stand. But the car took off again toward the dead end.

The Chrysler, having reached the road's limit, was now sliding to a halt. I locked the brakes up and cranked the wheel over hard to the left bringing the cruiser to a jolting stop abreast of the sedan. Training the spotlight on the perp's car, I opened my door, drew my service revolver just as the driver jumped out and made for the woods. Half laying over the windshield, I hollered as loud as I could, "FREEZE. DON'T MOVE." The man in the back seat quickly took my advice. My gut contracted and my arm muscles tensed as at any moment I expected to see muzzle flash from the woods.

Using the scout car as a shield, I began a series of shouted commands to try to control the situation. "ALL RIGHT NOW LISTEN UP. . .YOU, IN THERE . . . STICK YOUR HANDS OUT OF THE DOOR AND DON'T HAVE ANYTHING IN THEM. KEEP YOUR HANDS WHERE I CAN SEE THEM OR YOU'RE DEAD MEN."

All the while this was happening I knew the back-up cars were arriving by the sounds of their sirens, but split seconds seemed like hours. Upon my command only one man climbed out. Where was the third and where were the guns? I had the man out of the car and lying on the ground as the area filled with police cars in this normally quiet, dark, wooded, residential neighborhood. The robbers with the scattergun and handgun could be anywhere just waiting to blast any one of us at any moment. At times like this, the safety of the officers is primary to the rights of the suspects, so I knelt down next to the now handcuffed dude and placed my revolver at his head, saying, "If I or any other officer is shot by one of your buddies, I'm going to pull the trigger before I die . . . now tell me, where is the third guy and where are the guns?"

"He, he. . .got out at the top of the hill – he took the shotgun."

"How 'bout the driver?"

"No. No. The handgun's in the back seat."

Quickly, I got on the PA and announced, "All units on the scene, there's two additional subjects in the woods - one armed with a shotgun."

Shortly the canine unit from neighboring Blue Ash P.D. arrived and quickly found one of the missing robbers – the driver. The third man and the shotgun were still unaccounted for. The Chrysler was searched, turning up only the blue steel revolver and a wallet, but no money. The wallet contained the identification of one Jerry Curtis, a two-time loser, who was out on parole for armed robbery!

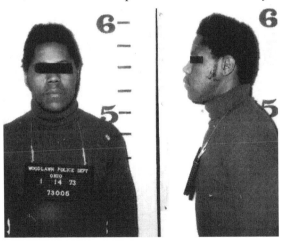

Two-time loser – the one with the Shotgun

The captured suspects were separated and transported to the station while LEOs from other departments inventoried the black over white sedan before having it towed to our impound lot.

Meanwhile at the station, the suspects, when confronted with the wallet, admitted to the robbery and that Curtis was the third man.

They both stated Curtis had instructed the driver to stop just over the crest of the hill so he could get out, with the shotgun, and shoot the officer who was chasing them – me! Now it dawned on me why the interior light came on. I felt a chill at the visualization of the squad car window shattering as I took a full charge of buckshot. For whatever reason, he booked it into the woods letting his compatriots fend for themselves.

The driver, one Elliston Whitson, last known address, Chicago, was also on parole for armed robbery. The back seat man was Emanual Pilder who had let Whitson drive the car belonging to Pilder's parents.

Jerry Curtis' parents lived within a mile of Rickman Road. Somewhere after 4:00 AM, with a couple of officers from an adjoining agency watching the back of the house, John and I rang the front door bell. A sleep-eyed Mrs. Curtis opened after we identified ourselves. We told her that the house was surrounded and that we believed her son Paul had been involved in an armed robbery and we had come to arrest him. She said she was sure he was asleep in his upstairs bedroom as she had heard him come home a few hours ago. Mrs. Curtis then led us down the narrow, dimly lit hall to the stairs. I called up for Jerry to come down – twice. No response. Turning to Mrs. Curtis, I said, "You go up and get him." Her reply set my adrenaline flowing for the second time this night: "Hell's fire, I'm ain't goin' up there. He shoot me, too!"

Summoning all the authority I could in my voice, I hollered up the steps: "JERRY CURTIS, POLICE OFFICERS . . . IF YOU DON'T COME DOWN BY THE TIME I COUNT TO THREE, WE'RE COMING UP AFTER YOU. WE KNOW YOU HAVE A SHOTGUN AND THE HOUSE IS SURROUNDED . . . ONE . . . TWO . . . THREE. There was no sound or movement. John whispered to me, "You go high, I'll go low." I nodded. It was time to do what only police officers get paid to do.

With handguns at the ready, my gut squeezed tight yet again, I stepped around the corner and into that stairwell . . . prepared to shoot at anything that moved. Starting up the steps with the full expectation of gunfire, a resigned voice called out from above, "Don't shoot, I'm coming down."

By 6:00 a.m. it was all over, the vehicle impounded, the prisoners in lock-up and the paper work under control – time for a cup o' joe at the Country Kitchen.

As I held the mug to warm my hands, I noticed they were shaking. Only then did I realize that I was scared. When it was happening – the chase, the confrontations, I didn't' have time to think about what might happen. Now I had the shakes. The feelings of fear, which didn't last long, were a good sign because it made me appreciate life a little more.

Jerry Curtis and Elliston Whitson went back to prison for 10 to 20 stretches. Emanuel Pilder, due to his co-operation and no prior convictions, got probation. The money and shotgun have never been found.

INJURED PERSON?

"Four-six-eight. Car 4-6-8, person injured, Woodlawn Food Market, Marion and Wayne. 4-6-8."

"Four-six-eight, okay," I responded to the dispatcher's detail. The time was late afternoon in our small southwestern Ohio village. It had been a quiet Saturday afternoon - one of those lazy spring days when cops do more waving and smiling than anything else. I turned my cruiser around, swung into traffic, and headed toward the food market.

Almost simultaneously my partner, 4-6-9, and I arrived to face a group of bystanders, some with coats, others in jackets and still others in shirt sleeves. It was that kind of day. In the morning it had been downright cold, but by mid-afternoon it was almost hot whenever those windows of ever-shifting and towering cumulus clouds parted enough to let the sun burn through.

"He's walking up there, on Wayne," one of the women in the crowd shouted, before we could even get out of our cars. Off we drove, not knowing who or what we're looking for. About a quarter mile away on this tree lined, narrow, two-lane road we came across a man carrying a coat and walking away from us. He had a nasty gash on the back of his head and blood had stained his shirt collar. We hit the roof lights to warn traffic and got out to talk to him.

"What happened?" I asked.

"He hit me with a bottle, almost killed me."

"Who hit you?"

"The man back there at the store. He stole my money and hit me in the head."

"Is he still there?" I asked becoming embarrassed that one of us should have stayed at the store to begin the investigation.

"Yeah, he's still there."

"Do you want me to call the life squad?"

"No, no. I ain't going to no hospital."

My partner, sensing the back-up of traffic and realizing someone has to return to the store to investigate a possible armed robbery took control.

"Patrolman Klein, why don't you take the gentleman back to the station for a statement and I'll return to the scene of the crime."

The heavy set man, about 50 years old, and still clutching what appeared to be a thick winter coat, reluctantly made himself at ease in the front seat of my patrol car. During the five minute ride to the station, and after advising the dispatcher of the situation, I made small talk trying to learn more about my passenger. Said he was retired, though he didn't look that old, and was living with his daughter in Lincoln Heights, an adjacent suburb.

Pulling into the station lot the radio broke squelch. I recognized my partner's identification as he broadcast, "Four-six-nine. Advise 4-6-8 his signal 22 is a signal 30. Request 4-8-4, signal 2, code 2 our office - assist 4-6-8."

My partner had told me the injured party was a wanted person and that it was serious enough that he was requesting assistance from another community! In retrospect, I guess I should have waited for the back-up to arrive. But hey, I was young and tough and besides the perp was already getting out of the scout car when the call came in.

Since he was bigger and he wasn't aware of his new status, I thought it might be better if we went inside. Entering the deserted squad room of the 1950's era police station, I ushered the perp to a

176

chair on the pretext of wanting to apply first aid to his scalp wound. At the same time I began assuring him that we'd get the guy that attacked him.

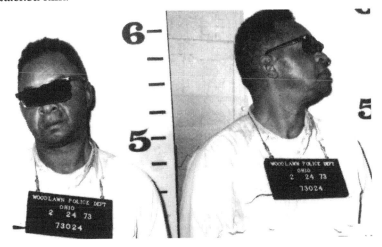

"Injured person?"

"Injured person's revolver"

Once seated, I knew the tactical position was mine. I reached for his coat that was now crumpled and lying on his lap while saying, "Let me take this. It will make you more comfortable, sir." As I pulled at the heavy wool material, I could now see the man's hand was wrapped around a revolver!

Instinctively I grabbed for it, he shoved at me with his left arm then everything seemed to be happening in slow motion. I could see my hand going for the perp's gun as the barrel slowly rotated toward me. I was trying to balance myself for the thrust of the perp's free elbow all the while my right hand raced to my service revolver. At the same time I was aware that my mind was screaming, why is it taking so long? My right hand clawed at the security strap on the Jordan holster. I seized the custom gripped three-fifty-seven magnum, again wondering why it was taking such an inordinate amount of time to clear leather. I heard my voice hollering, "LET GO! LET GO! LET GO!" I had what I hoped was a death grip on the gun-in-the-coat. The man was strong, I wasn't gaining an advantage, my Smith & Wesson started toward his throat, trigger finger tightening. The pending explosion of one or both weapons was imminent.

"LET GO! LET GO!" I knew as soon as my Model 19 reached battery it was going off. The magnum slammed into the perp's neck, my souped-up mind was telling my unreasonably slow trigger finger: PULL, PULL, PULL.

The man relaxed, his gun hand released, he stopped shoving . . . and in that nano-second, through my mind flashed: kill him, he tried to kill you, they'll make you a hero, blow him away, kill him. But over-riding this subconscious speed-of-light musing was a deeper inner articulation: American police officer, fair play, the rule of law, the right thing to do.

By the time I had the assaulting weapon secured and was ordering the perp to lie face down on the floor the backup had arrived. We searched and cuffed him and threw him in the holding cell. My partner walked in as I began telling the sequence of events. He picked up the signal 30's revolver, opened it, looked at the loaded cylinder and said as he showed it to me, "you're a lucky guy."

The primer that had been under the hammer was dented - it had been struck by the firing pin. The man had pulled the trigger in an attempt to shoot me. But, because either the coat or my hand had impaired the fall of the hammer, it was a few ounces shy of striking hard enough to cause detonation.

178

I think it was then my knees got a little weak and irate thoughts raced through my mind of how this dirt bag had tried to kill me. This was followed by anger at myself for not blowing him away when I had the chance. If I had put the scum two-seven, I would be hailed a hero for taking a potential cop-killer off the streets and for surviving, for all intents and purposes, a firefight.

Turns out the perp, a walk-away from a mental hospital, had tried to steal goods from the food market and when confronted by the store owner, pulled the revolver on him. The proprietor, in self-defense, grabbed a pop bottle and hit the robber on the head. The store owner yelled for someone to call the police. A customer, who had only seen a bleeding man walking out of the store, called to report what she'd observed, merely, an "injured man."

There were no newspaper reports of the incident - like confrontations happen to police officers every day. My scrapbook doesn't contain any commendations of heroism, but I know, inside myself, I did the right thing and that's hero enough.

FOR THOSE WE SERVE

1975 R90/6, 900cc, BMW Motorcycle

Convertibles are great, sports cars even better, but a motorcycle is best for pure motoring fun. Decked out in torn, ragged denim work pants and a sleeveless shirt, I looked and felt like a hardened outlaw biker as I crossed the dam bridge into Warsaw, a gritty Ohio River town back dropped by the mountainous hills and valleys of Kentucky.

Serving process (finding and personally delivering subpoenas or summons) is always an iffy proposition especially for private investigators. Cops have radios, back-up and the color of law; PIs don't. Sometimes I've had to resort to elaborate scams and cover stories in order to be able to swear that the named person had in fact been served. In past cases I had employed various pretexts, including posing as a worker's union official and a sweepstakes front man. The latter had been cruel because the target's wife had really believed they were about to share in the Reader's Digest jackpot.

Other times things can get hairy. Private investigators usually only get the summons or subpoenas when the Sheriff's office can't locate the person. Working alone and without any form of radio backup, finding losers who don't want to be found can lead to dangerous conditions. I was, however, never without at least one handgun.

"Hi. Where can I find Eve?"

The bag boy glanced around while bagging groceries for a matronly looking farmer's wife who covered me with a disdainful stare.

"I'm not sure. I don't think she comes in 'till eleven. Ask the manager - he's over there," the kid said, nodding toward the bread racks.

Eleven it is. Maybe a cup of coffee at the Bun Boy across the street and a few phone calls will help kill some time. I had gotten a tip that the target's girlfriend, Eve, worked at this IGA. The target was the guy named in the summons in my pocket. I wasn't privy to particulars of the case; my job was to serve process.

A few minutes before the hour I parked my R90/6 BMW in the back of the IGA lot where employees would usually park, sat on the ground leaning against the MC and watched. The bike fit my image, sort of: scruffy and rough - not some shiny, primped sissified bad-boy-wannabe's ride. Right on time an old beater with a woman driver, you could hardly call her a chick, drove in and parked two spaces to my left. Take away the clean, starched uniform and she'd look like she'd seen a few too many miles from the back of a Harley.

"Hey, Eve baby, how ya doin'? It's Char," I said to her quizzical frown. Making up stuff as I went along in hopes of gaining her trust, I continued, "You know, we met up at the Roundup a while back. I'm looking for your old man. Where can I find him?"

With her lip twisted and a squint, she replied, "Char? Wasn't you at the pig roast up to Cecil's place back a couple of months ago?"

"Yeah, I was there too. But I thought I also saw you at the Roundup," I ad-libbed.

"Look, I'm gonna be late for work, ah what... ."

"I was just wondering where I can find your old man."

"First off, I ain't got no old man no more, and second, I don't know, much less care where the hell he is. Nice bike you got."

With the knowledge that she and Knueson were on the outs I put on my best smile. "Well, if you ain't seein' him no more maybe you and me could toss a few down sometime?"

She turned toward me thrusting her hip out, "Yeah, maybe we could at that . . . Char. Why don't you stop back around nine when I get off work?"

"I can't tonight baby. But ah, I'd like to take a rain check. Where can I find Bobby? He promised to put me on to his main man."

"Have you tried his farm? And he ain't got a main man. He's the main man if you catch my drift. He grows the stuff his self, right there. But don't tell him I told ya or he'll kill me. Know what I mean, honey? The farm is down around Bee Camp Hollar - over to Switzerland County. The name on the mailbox is the name William Cusper - that's the name he uses."

She smiled through chipped, nicotine stained teeth as I smiled back thinking I wouldn't't take her to a dog fight – even if she was the main attraction.

Some clouds, along with the humidity, had begun to roll in, but as long as I kept the Beemer moving, it was comfortable enough. All along I had been under the impression he lived in Kentucky; Switzerland County, Indiana, just across the river from Warsaw, is where I live.

It took a stop to chat with the Vevay police department to learn that William R. Cusper was only known as such. A check at the courthouse provided the information that a William Cusper did in fact own 178 acres on Bee Camp plus another 40 in Posey Township. Neither of the properties was encumbered by any liens. There was no record of Bobby Knueson. The man might be a drug manufacturing, biker-sleeze bag, but he was smart enough to keep his real identity secret from the locals. Even though the subpoena in my pocket only had the name of Bobby Knueson, it would still be good as long as I added the a.k.a.

The hollar looked just like the name sounded - down-home, unsophisticated good 'ol boy country. The rusty mailbox with the crudely hand painted name, Cusper, was perched atop an old stump. The farm house, if you could call it that, was visible back a short dirt drive. The house was really an older double-wide that could use a little sprucing up. A polished Harley Sportster and a dusty, but well cared for, late model Ford F-150 pick-up truck were parked off to the side and in front of a weathered, wood-sided barn.

I secured the BMW near the mailbox and walked to the trailer. The door was standing open so I called, then yelled for Mr. Cusper. Dirty dishes were scattered throughout the kitchen and living room as were articles of clothing, beer cans and an empty pizza box. What really caught my attention was the AR15 or M16 rifle, I couldn't tell which, and handfuls of ammunition lying on the stained, sun faded sofa.

The barn was also void of any living creatures, disturbingly quiet save for the sound of a tractor. I walked in the direction of the noise which came from around back of the barn and a stand of cedars. In the adjoining field was a man on a red and silver trimmed Massey Ferguson diesel tractor pulling a sixty-inch bush hog. The operator, a man of about forty, throttled back as I approached. Above the din of the tractor and rotating blades I shouted, "William Cusper?"

"Yeah, what do you want?" the man hollered back. He was a burly man with large, dark eyes and curly, black hair that was matted with sweat. On his upper arm was the tattoo of an eagle. He pulled a blue bandanna from a hip pocket and wiped a neck that was as thick as a tractor tire.

Producing the court paper from a back pocket, I handed it to Cusper, saying, "Thanks, you've been served."

Before I could back away, the man shoved it back shouting, "I ain't Mr. Cusper. I thought you was ah askin' if this was his place. He's gone for now but will be back around sundown."

Since I didn't have any physical description of the man and no other way to identify him, I had to take the subpoena back or risk a bad service. Before I could ask any more questions the tractor had been set into motion again, forcing me to step out of the way.

At the county road I fired up the BMW and rode on back the hollar while my mind worked at trying to come up with a new pretext or a different twist to an old one. About a quarter mile away, a middle-aged woman in overalls was tending a large vegetable garden in front of a neat, clean frame house. I stopped at her gravel drive and, while fighting the chipped stone to secure the kick-stand, the lady approached. "May I help you?"

"Yes, thank you. I'm looking for Billy Cusper. Do you know where I can find him?"

"Why, yes. That's him on that tractor over there," she said, pointing to the field I had just come out of.

Sometimes ya get lucky. By the time I'd turned the heavy bike around on the narrow one lane road, cruised back to the rusty mailbox and secured the kick-stand once again, Cusper was standing next to the pick-up. Leaving my bike running, and the subpoena concealed in my left hand, I strode right at the 250 pound tractor operator/biker. A man who out-weighted me by at least 75 pounds and was taller by 3-4 inches.

"Did you find him, man? I tell ya he won't be back 'till much later. I'll tell him… ."

In mid-sentence, and now within striking distance, I stuffed the court order in the man's shirt pocket, spitting out, "You're Knueson and you've been served, Bobby!"

The roundhouse blow was easy to duck because, like any good cop or P.I., I was ready for it. Now all I wanted to do was get out of there with the minimum amount of damage. Mr. Knueson/Cusper had different ideas. Most perpetrators, once you've beaten them by either placing them under arrest or serving them with process, would curse and yell, call you a few choice names and sometimes take a half-poke at you just to show that they went down swinging like a real man. The guys who don't say anything are the perps you have to look out for. Knueson was silent.

184

Recovering from the missed punch, Bobby stepped back and without a moment's hesitation, grabbed an iron bar from the bed of the pick-up, raised it above his head and again advanced.

"Look man, I don't want no trouble. I'm just doin' my job," I growled, as I backed away and into a scrub tree I hadn't noticed before. The action shifted into slow motion, a pseudo time deception phenomena known as tachyinterval. Frustration is rampant under this unique condition when events appear to occur in slow motion because the brain is processing more information than the body can react to in a timely manner. I knew the iron bar was coming, knew I couldn't back away in time, knew I had to get my gun out and that the man meant to kill me. But I couldn't understand why it was taking so long to extract the 2 ½ inch barreled Diamondback from my hip holster. Both combatants knew, tachyinterval or not, that once the gun cleared the scabbard and came into battery it was going to explode with flesh tearing, lethal results. Like most important events in life, timing is everything.

At the instant before the revolver, stuffed full of Hornady 125 grain hollow points, reached the point-shoulder position, the thug let the bar fall. The look in Knueson's eyes signaled only temporary surrender as his vengeful stare locked on the vent-ribbed blued steel instrument of death still pointed at him. As we slowly backed away from each other, he toward the double-wide where the rifle and ammunition lay ready on a couch, me toward the still idling bike, Knueson uttered a string of venomous words to the effect that he'd kill me.

Thankful that I had left the bike running while fearful of stalling the engine with a nerve tingling clutch hand, I turned and ran for the Beemer.

Postscript: The a.k.a. information coupled with the location of the two farms allowed the complainant to file liens which caused Knueson to spread it around that he was going to 'get me'. As it turned out, Knueson and I had a mutual friend who invited both of us to his wedding – Switzerland County had less than 7000 inhabitants and everyone knew someone who knew someone. Knowing of the bad blood between us, the friend made us both promise not to cause any trouble at the nuptials. I didn't have a problem with that, but I still packed my Colt Diamondback - and my backup gun, a S&W M36, in an ankle holster.

185

CLOSE ENCOUNTERS OF THE
HEART-STOPPING KIND

Smith & Wesson .357 Magnum Revolver

The second to last thing a morally responsible, prudent
person wants to do is kill another human being regardless
of how reprehensible, villainous or dangerous that
person might be. The last thing this morally responsible,
prudent person wants to do is be killed by that
reprehensible, villainous and dangerous person.

KA-POW, KA-POW, KA-POW the sound of the .357 Magnum reverberated off the walls of the family room. I reached for... the remote to terminate the inane slaughter of television violence.

Killing... the room lights brought instant darkness to compliment the deafening quiet as I stepped out onto the deck. Now the only sound to penetrate the solitude of our secluded haven on the shores of Goose Creek Bay, was that of a Great Horned Owl and the light rustling of leaves from the wisps of a soft summer breeze.

Complacency and tranquility could only describe my feelings as I followed the planking surrounding this picture-windowed cedar home, nestled among the trees of our 144 acre Hoosier farm. Admiring the view of the Kentucky hills across the Ohio River and its smattering of manmade lights, I walked the length of the deck to our bedroom.

After undressing in preparation to shower, I moved back outside to gather some towels that had been left to dry on the rail earlier in the day. Turning to retrace the two steps to the bedroom's sliding-screen door, I was stunned to see the outline of a man, his feet firmly planted, standing halfway down the deck. A quick glance was all I needed to see that this invader of placidity was about my size, had heavy, dark, bushy hair and . . . AND he had something in his hand, AND that something, was pointing at me!

Having been a police officer and a private investigator I've been in tight spots before, but standing naked on my own property, this guy really got my attention! With my eyes riveted on the thing leveled at me while struggling to reach the door, I yelled, "WHO ARE YOU . . . GET OUT OF HERE." He didn't say anything and as best I could see his expressionless blank stare didn't change.

Stumbling, crashing, running into the house, slamming the screen door closed behind me, I saw out of the corner of my eye, that the trespasser was now advancing toward my end of the deck. The thoughts that went through my mind as I raced to the bureau where I kept a gun ran from . . ."Surely it's a friend playing a joke on me and he's going to burst out laughing any second," to . . ." this could only be a sleaze bag from some past arrest or investigation who had sworn to get me."

Cedar River Farm, Patriot, IN, 1980

In what seemed like an inordinate amount of time, I reached the dresser - hang on now - just give me half a second. The muscles in my back tensed in preparation for the bullet that was sure to come as my brain strained to scan all enemies, past and present.

Snatching the .357 Magnum from a drawer full of socks, I whirled around, dropped to the floor behind the bed and came up with the classic two-hand hold directed at the screen door whose frame was now filled by the stranger. The silent stranger with something in his hand.

Again I hollered for the man to leave or tell me what he wanted or who he was - anything. No response. He just stood there in the shadows while the harsh incandescence light from the bathroom spotlighted me. Now, I could detect that the ominous object in his hand had something sticking out of it - like a barrel!

I waited, listening, looking for the flash of fire that was certainly only moments away. Maybe the screen will deflect the bullet, maybe he'll miss, maybe... . The years of police indoctrination took hold as I resigned myself to empty my gun into this intruder before I died. I strained to see, almost hoping to discern a flash of fire that would bring this confrontation to a very climatic and final end. My death threat didn't move, didn't make a sound. The screen rippled. It might have been the wind. The hair on the back of my neck stood up.

I had to think, go over my options, form a plan, I couldn't take my eyes off the thing in his hand. Surely this isn't real - too much TV!

I didn't have to shoot unless he shot first or unless I was sure it was a weapon he was holding and he gave some indication that he was going to use it. Since I was home alone I could even allow him to enter the house, and as long as he didn't try to get too close or actually assault me, I could just play this thing out. I really wanted to know who he was . . . and, why?

The bed afforded enough cover that I didn't want to risk trying for the phone to call the sheriff or a neighbor - the nearest being over a half mile to the west. Besides the police would be at least 20 minutes away since there was only one on-duty officer for the entire county. I could make a dash for the hallway where I could hide, but if he shot me as I ran I wouldn't be able to return the favor. Besides he could hide too and wait until I went to bed or my wife and sons came home and then attack.

Half lying, half sitting, still undressed, light shining on me and my legs beginning to cramp, I continued to shout, "WHO ARE YOU... WHAT DO YOU WANT...GET OUT OF HERE OR I'LL BLOW YOU AWAY, MAN!"

My imagination was running wild. Maybe he was just guarding the door so the real perp could slip in the front and sneak up behind me. I tried to be cognizant of my peripheral vision, lest I take my eyes from what has to be some form of lethal and instant destruction hidden by the screen. I held my breath so not even the sound of my breathing could mask another invader.

Then, still without so much as a word, he turned and started back down the deck. In a flash I killed the light in the bathroom and pulled on a pair of shorts then ran toward the hall. I don't know why I took the time to put on my briefs, but it made me feel better, less vulnerable.

Reaching the entrance way, I saw through the kitchen window, that he had made the end of the deck. He froze as I covered him with light from the driveway floods while opening the door and taking careful aim. He was less than twenty feet from me now and I could see what was in his hand. It was a pencil and pad of paper.

He could have been killed. I might have shot him. My head felt hot and at the same time a chill came over my whole body. I'd had men in my sights before, but this was different. I was just doing my job then, this was personal - this was home to my wife and children!

I motioned for him to come over where he displayed a message on the pad reading, "My Father says I'm a very special person". The stranger was a mentally handicapped, deaf mute!

Keeping my distance I put the gun down and took his pad. After writing notes back and forth he finally told me who he was. He seemed shy, so I invited him in the kitchen for a Coke while I telephoned his family who promised to send someone right up. I learned from further note writing that he had often admired our house from the road and just wanted to see it up close. He had driven his car only part way up the quarter mile driveway, with his lights out, and had walked the rest of the way.

End of story? Not quite. The next day I learned that he was a walk-away from a state mental hospital, committed by his family because he was prone to violence and had attacked people during previous encounters. On this occasion he had savagely beaten his aged father before stealing the car he used to visit me. His brother told me the family wouldn't have held it against me if I had killed him.

I was relieved that the taking of a human life hadn't been necessary, but I was also comforted that I had subscribed to the old country adage: "The door might not always be locked, but the gun is always loaded". Maybe he had wanted more than just a look, but the gun scared him. What if the gun hadn't been available or what if the kids or my wife had been home and one of them had been the first to encounter him, what if... .

> *If you're ever in a situation where another person*
> *is about to murder you, at that moment,*
> *you'd trade all your worldly possessions*
> *for a firearm. And, if that threat was to kill your child*
> *or your grandchild, you'd sell your soul for a gun.*

Author's Detective Badge and Colt .38 Special Diamondback Revolver

WORKIN' HONEYS

1972 Chevrolet El Camino

My first glimpse of her, of all places, was on a used car lot. Nonetheless, it was love at first sight. But I worried. Had she been abused? Her interior ripped? Have a lot of miles? Rust, dirty oil, and other signs of neglect? First off, I realize calling a truck "she" might not seem logical. I mean, trucks are supposed to be brawny, tough, rugged and all those other masculine things.

El Caminos, however, are all of those, plus they're sort of like a young, lithe Olympian swimmer in her skin tight suit – muscle and curves most prominent along with that feminine mystic.

It was fall, 1972 and with both my wife and I working, we were finally in a position to buy a new car. What I had always wanted was an El Camino, but the '73 models were lame. They had huge doors, no cozy wings, protruding bumpers and, well, they just weren't cool. The '72s, on the other hand, were better made and much healthier looking.

On my way home from picking up a few groceries late on a warm afternoon, I happened to notice a copper with black vinyl roof and silver rockers 1972 model conspicuously displayed on a used car lot. I wheeled in and tried to contain my excitement when I saw the odometer at only 4000 miles. The plaid-shirted-striped-tie-white-soxed salesman sensed my want . . . my need for this truck. He told me she was a re-pop and he was going to wholesale it the next day. The price was as much as a new one, but it did have all the right extras: A/C, A/T, rally wheels, air shocks, a bench seat and 350-V8. There were no negotiations as he was firm on the price – somehow knowing I had to have this almost new, last-of-its breed El Camino. I gave him all the cash I had on me, $55, as a down payment. We signed some papers and he said it would take two days to get the title and financing.

As soon as I got home, I checked the weather reports for hurricanes, fires or tornado warnings for the next two days. So, I'm a little paranoid. But, just because one is paranoid, doesn't mean they aren't after you or bad stuff won't happen.

Two days later – to the minute – I arrived at the used car dealer to overhear the sales manager telling someone on the phone that he had a black-over-copper 1972 El Camino that he was offering to sell for $200 more than I had a contract for! I barged into his office and said, "What are you doing?" He put his hand over the mouthpiece saying, "I can get $200 more – do you want to pony up or should I let this guy I've got on the phone have it?

I was wearing jeans and a short-sleeve shirt, but as a patrolman with a suburban police department, I always carried my credentials in a badge case (and a concealed gun, of course). Grabbing it out of my back pocket and flashing the tin on him, I said, in my most authoritative voice, "I'm a police officer . . . and I'll bet I can fit a crime to what you're trying to do."

Looking a little flushed, he put the phone down without saying goodbye to whomever (if anyone) was on the line. He stammered that the paperwork wasn't complete and I'd have to come back the next day. I tossed the keys to my trade-in on his desk and commanded, "Put a dealer tag on the El Camino, I'm taking it now. Call me when the paper work is ready and I'll bring your plate back."

I played with this workin' honey for ten years logging 100K miles. I then gave her to my son when he got his license at age 16. He also drove it ten years and put another 100K miles on her – until some uninsured drunk in his loser-mobile ran a stop sign and T-boned him. My son wasn't hurt, but the workin' honey was totaled. In those 200K miles and 20 years we replaced all the hang-on stuff a couple of times, did a re-paint and seat covers, but never put a wrench to the drive train.

Almost twenty-five years later finds me beginning retirement on a farm in southwestern Ohio. Needing transportation in the form of a truck to haul grandkids And supplies, I began a hunt for a fully restored non-SS, pre '73 El Camino.

From an ad in Old Car News, I found a 1971 model within 500 miles. After some phone negotiations, my son and I drove the trade-in to the classic car dealer, made the test drive and then drove her home. This black beauty has a vinyl roof, factory crate 350–V8, A/C, A/T, air shocks, and most of all, a bench seat. The bench seat was important so as three could ride in the front – grandkids love that.

Author's 1971 Chevrolet El Camino at Kamp Klein Farm, Georgetown, OH 2014

194

The guy who did the body-off restoration added 15" mag wheels, but I found a set of 14" rally wheels and returned it to stock. I've since added the statutorily required amenities – a spotlight and oil/amp/temp gauges to replace the idiot lights. Hey, I used to be a cop and I know the law :)

Interior of Author's 1971 Chevrolet El Camino

For what I paid for this second workin' honey, I could have bought a fully tricked-out F-150 or Silverardo. But, that was eight years ago and those "new" trucks are surely worth significantly less today. As I log only about a thousand miles per year, the '71 will always be worth at least what I paid for it. Besides, out here on these two-lane county roads, with the cozy wing cranked wide open and my arm on the window sill, I really get a kick out of kicking down into passing gear to dust off a John Deere pulling a wagon load of hay. See, you really can go home again.

For the 1959 model year, Chevrolet begins to sell a car-truck hybrid that it calls the El Camino. Impressed by sales of the Ford Ranchero, which had already been on the market for two years, the El Camino, likewise, was a combination sedan-pickup truck built on a full-sized chassis. Chevy ads at the time championed: "The most beautiful thing that ever shouldered a load!" "It rides and handles like a convertible, yet hauls and hustles like the workingest thing on wheels."

Ford's Ranchero was the first "car-truck" sold in the United States, but it was not a new idea. Since the 1930s, Australian farmers had been driving what they called "utes" – short for "coupé utility" – all around the outback.

Legend has it that a farmer's wife from rural Victoria, Australia, had written a letter to Ford, asking the company to build a car that could carry her to church on Sundays and her husband's pigs to market on Mondays. In response, Ford engineer Lewis Brandt designed a low-slung sedan-based vehicle that was a ritzy passenger car in the front, with wind-up windows and comfortable seats and a rough-and-tumble pickup in back.

El Caminos production history:

1st generation (1959–1960) Full size Impala chassis.

2nd generation (1964–1967) Scaled down to the Malibu chassis.

3rd generation (1968–1972) Last model produced with cozy (wind) wings.

4th generation (1973–1977) Very lame due to NHTSA safety/fuel regs.

5th generation (1978–1987) No El Caminos have been produced since.

WASN'T FUNNY AT THE TIME

Medical Helicopter

I just got back from a visit to the Southwest Regional/Marginal Medical/Hospital (used to be known as Brown County General Hospital). I don't know why they had to change the name, I mean BCGH says all you need to know. It would be like calling Apple computers pears or cucumbers. Anyway, I was scheduled for a stress test at 7:15 in the morning - the only time they say the test can be originated. But some caring person called me a few days before to say if I got there at 8 a.m. that would be just fine. In and of itself, that lowered my stress level.

Though the doctor's main practice is in Cincinnati, I choose BCGH because I want to keep my business local. Registration was quick and easy and after a short wait of maybe 10 minutes (another advantage to living in a small town) I was readied for some kind of scan. They put me on a flat bed with crispy-clean sheets and allowed a huge box-machine to revolve inches above my chest - stress level up. The

197

nurse/technician, Tammy, told me I would be under this thing for 20 minutes and I should breathe normally, but could not move.

Ever try to breathe normally when you're thinking about it? What's normal? Tammy told me she would be in the room the entire time which reduced my stress - until I thought maybe she's staying to make sure I breathe normally. I fixated on a spot in the ceiling and built (in my head) the walnut cabinet I've been meaning to make someday. Time flies when you're having fun - at least that's what a jailer once told me.

Next, I was taken to the actual test room to be prepped for the walk-a-thon. Here, a nurse attached wires to patches stuck to my chest while another person inserted an IV in my arm to inject stuff to allow the stress machine to monitor my heart. I've got wires pasted to me, a needle in my arm, had nothing to eat or drink since last night and I'm freezing cold - stress city.

In due time the doctor arrived and onto the treadmill I went. At first the stride was like a nice stroll in a park, but without the trees and grass. Just as soon as I began to relax with the pace they sped up the machine while adding an incline. At least I wasn't chilled any longer, beads of sweat now forming on my forehead. However, in all too long a time, the treadmill speed not only increased a second time, but so was the angle. I was now in double-overdrive - walking as fast as I could - up hill and wishing the room was cooler. At 14 hours, seven minutes and nine seconds into the test, I finally heard the doctor say, "stops in 10 seconds." Did he mean the machine or my heart? Fortunately, before I was totally stressed out, they lowered the ramp and slowed the tread way down. Whew! Wait... I lied about the 14 hour part - I was only on the treadmill a total of eight minutes, but it seemed a mite longer.

It seems stress tests are only relevant for the exact time and place it is administered. It's now four years later and severe pain awoke me at seven o'clock in the morning. My chest hurt as did my jaw - classic heart-attack symptoms. Clutching my 72 year-old most-vital fluid-pump, I made it to the fridge, found the tiny nitro tablets and dissolved two under my tongue. My bad. I should have taken only one. A few minutes later, I felt light headed and immediately sat down. My adult son, home for Thanksgiving, came in to make his morning coffee and I was able to mumble "heart-attack" before passing out. My wife and son called 9-1-1 while trying to revive me and get me to swallow an aspirin. They determined I was breathing and had a faint heartbeat, but was unresponsive for about 20 minutes.

Soon the Brown County Life Squad arrived. The EKG and vital sign check determined it would be best to transport me to Mercy Anderson Hospital – via helicopter. Normally, I would be imagining this was going to be really cool as I have never been in a whirlybird, however, I was really thinking . . . are we there yet. My wife gathered my wallet with medical cards and a bag of snackies (she knew it might be a long day), and headed for the hospital in her car.

The squad took me to the heliport at what had been Brown County General where the chopper was waiting for us. The crews traded wires, tubes, bedding and paraphernalia with the copter team. Seems each medical service, as well as each hospital department, always wants their gear back. Having been a cop, I can relate – cops always retain their own handcuffs when exchanging prisoners.

The ten minute Air Evac ride was – to an old-timer - akin to the overnight passenger trains of the 40s and 50s. There was motion and noise, but as on a Pullman of old, it was soothing inasmuch as it could lull you to sleep. Laying flat on a stretcher my view was just farm land on the horizon. The pilot was so skilled, there was virtually no sensation of liftoff or landing, but I know we banked at least once - only because I saw the Court House.

Upon arrival at Mercy Anderson, I could see my wife waiting for me – it's a one hour drive from our farm. She either had to drive very fast or the transfer took longer than I thought.

In the ER, I heard one of the staff say they were going to give me Plavix. I recognized the word as a drug advertised on TV. There's also another drug that gets a lot of TV time, but I couldn't remember the name. Since Plavix sounded familiar, I asked, "Am I going to get lucky? Is that the drug that if it lasts longer than four hours I should call my doctor." It got a laugh.

Now stabilized, I was wheeled to the Cath department for a carotid angioplasty. The doctor explained, as he hefted a scalpel that

199

looked like a machete, that they were going to jam a camera inside my artery to view the heart from the inside. You've seen cameras the news media sling over their shoulders . . . wait, I lied about the machete part and the camera wasn't exactly that large and it was more like precision threading than jamming.

I didn't feel a thing – except for the blood pressure band. Because they had two IVs in my left arm and the camera was going in my right arm, they put the BP on my calf. They forgot to tell me. The first time it pumped up, I thought it was a Charlie Horse. During the 2-day, 6-hour procedure it tightened up every ten seconds and hurt like the dickens. Well . . . maybe I exaggerated a mite. Actually the whole thing took perhaps 30 minutes and the BP only went off three or four times – but it really did hurt.

Finally, around two P.M. they put me in a semi-private room where I was allowed a meal. Soon, the Hospitalist (I think that's what they call the resident MD) paid me a visit with the good news that all was well and he was releasing me. The doctor walks out, I start to sit up in bed and my RN says, "Where do you think you're going?"

"The doctor said I could go home."

"You're not going anywhere until the bleeding stops."

Bleeding? I didn't know I was bleeding. I quickly tugged at my gown sleeve to inspect what surely had to be a gaping hole where the media camera had been wedged in. Truthfully, I had to put my bifocals on to see the incision. My RN firmly and gently explained that the photo-op of the inside of my heart was via an artery and it takes a few hours to seal. Doctors might be the head honcho at hospitals, but it's the RNs who really call the shots and run things.

Seven P.M. and I'm on my way home – with written instructions saying if the artery starts to bleed I should apply direct pressure and call 9-1-1. It didn't say how to hold your thumb on the hole in your wrist and operate a phone at the same time, but I didn't even want to think about such things.

It started out Tuesday morning as a dull ache in my upper jaw/face bone area. By noon, it was bothersome and I took some aspirin, and again at 4:00. Six o'clock there was noticeable swelling and pain to the point of not thinking clearly. Fortunately, my wife, a retired dental officer manager, surmised it might be a root canal. I didn't want to hear that.

Last RC I had, about 40 years ago, is still a very painful and vivid memory: They strapped me into what looked like the Sing-Sing electric chair and then with hammer and chisel began what could only be described in today's vernacular as a criminal assault. Oh sure, they stuck a huge needle in my gum saying it was Novocain and I wouldn't feel a thing. They lied . . . and maybe I exaggerated just a touch about the conditions, but it was significant pain. Then I had to come back in a week for the crown. They allowed a week 'cuz that's about the time it takes for the jaw to stop hurting from being jammed open for the jack-hammer.

I phoned my dentist's office and got the recording to push 'one' if this is an emergency to leave a message. He called within a few minutes and said he'd call in an antibiotic prescription to CVS and, with his wife at his side, determined they could fit me in Thursday morning.- she's the brains behind the management.

Under the expertise of this expert dentist, not only was it a one stop shopping experience, but the pain was less than a teeth cleaning, not that a cleaning ever hurts. My dentist, Bart, whom I've known since high school, is a technophobe and thus has the latest and most innovative equipment available. For example, X-Rays are instantly displayed in HD on a TV screen. Also, they have a magic wand (can't come up with a better description) they wave over the worked-on tooth and, in an hour, a machine manufactures a perfect-fit crown. Or, in my case, a plug to go in the hole they drilled in the crown to get at the infected root. Bart tells me he will have 3-D X-Ray equipment later this year. I hope it comes with action figures!

In appreciation of his professional care, I took him lunch at Bob Evans and told him he can have anything on the menu – hey I can be a sport! I even chewed on the plugged tooth and never noticed any discomfort.

Next time you need your teeth cleaned, your roots tweaked or anything done that you use your mouth for . . . no, wait this needs a little more editing.

Hope you enjoyed my stories, Chuck

Postscript

Writing the stories and putting this book together forced a lot of memories, many of which are directly or indirectly related to music.

Usually and unsuspectingly the melody of an old favorite can trigger that certain flashback to another lifetime; a day, an hour or just an instant to which only you can relate. A special moment, jarring somewhere in the beyond of your own individual history that just you can memorialize; a clear-cut reminiscence that can't be shared with anyone because it's solitarily exclusive to you. Be it the ambient, ear-candy rumble of the drag strip or the smile on your face as you listen to the engine you tuned; the knowledge of experiencing a noteworthy event - noteworthy because it was so private and remarkable at the time.

Saturday night, sometime after ten, *Come on Baby Let the Good Times Roll* blares over the vacuum tube radio in the garage as I struggle to figure out how to finish my hot rod. I wash my hands with gasoline, sit against the rear tire and wish the good times would roll for me—roll with any of the dream girls in my high school class as we rip down the drag strip. I visualized the pert brunette with the high pony tail wrapped in my arms or the blonde next door snuggling up close, the hot rod smoking its tires. The good times, I fail to realize, were happening right then – I was 15, building a car of my own, a member of the rock & roll generation and dreaming dreams. For sure, I later had girlfriends and raced my car, but that twinkling of fantasies still stands alone. There are very few who can realize and recognize they are living in the good-old-days as they materialize.

Looking back 60-50-40-30 … years, the audio trip-wires deep in the mind's back-gears are comprised of friends—even enemies—or just-by-yourself sunrises, sunsets and yesterday's lifetimes. No one has yet captured these inside-the-head musings on film, paper or even modern electronic media—these feelings that cut to the soul. They're so distinctive and exclusive we can't share them with others because words fail to translate sensitivities of spirits.

Paul Anka's, *Put Your Head On My Shoulder,* is playing on one of those fifties radio programs, only I hear it whispering from the AM of my almost new '57 Ford V8. We're on a narrow two-lane state road, dash lights dimmed, high beams on, cozy-wings cracked; speed about 70. She scoots across the wide bench seat ...and puts her head on my shoulder. Approaching an older and slower car, I flash my lights, he moves over; and just for fun, I kick it down and top out a bit over 90. Hearing the song in my mind's ear 50 some years later — ah Sharon, our teenage love was so sweet. Except that Sharon, like so many others from that past lifetime, has passed on. Could life, could this slice of time that I've never forgotten, have been any better?

Some nostalgic flashbacks are so specific they are non-emulative. I'm alone in an Ermine-white Corvette on a moonlit night, rolling down a twisting mountain road—headlights out, engine off. Superimposed over the wind and whine of the tires the beat of Chuck Berry's, *Maybelline,* surges from the custom installed RCA record player. It's just me, the machine, the High Sierras and exhilarations that live only inside my head. How many lifetimes ago was that? I've lost count, but whenever I hear that piece of ear-candy ....

Engelbert Humperdinck, long sideburns, Go-Go boots, big-block Chevys and just married—times we thought belonged only to us. There was no realization, just like my teenage years, that I was establishing memories of a honeymoon-like eon. A warm late spring afternoon we pack a picnic basket and head to the woods. Between nips of wine and slivers of cheese we make love to the echo of a warbler and the pecking of a woodpecker. That was two or three lifetimes ago; nonetheless my mind's ear still hears the trill and the tap, tap, tap. Nothing lasts forever and being able to move on—to have the ability to adapt to change is a learned secret.

The second-time-around, after a short span of middle age singing and dancing with a variety of petite, tall, buxom, hot ... you get the picture; I found a soul mate. To a Johnny Mathis song we promised, accepted and committed to the *Twelfth of Never.* Now, almost 20 years into this marriage, we share memories of the lifetime when our combined children were birthing their children and we lived downtown in that portion of the city still being gentrified. We enjoyed Saturday night always-armed walks to Music Hall to hear a world class symphony followed by a cup of herbal tea and a scone at a 19th Century bar turned bistro where a three-piece combo characterized charming.

During a magical span of about ten years movie goers were privileged to such musical lollipops as *West Side Story, Oklahoma, South Pacific, My Fair Lady, The King and I, The Sound of Music* and many others; some of which insightfully touched on society ills. Like kids in a world-sized candy store we were historically oblivious. The genius of the music, lyrics and choreography of this era created an unparalleled period that now spans generations as we DVR these classics for our grandchildren.

Talented poets, song writers and novelist are masters of describing extraordinary moments. However, their soul-exposing feelings belong to them, not you and me. What we experience from their performances are prompts to our own recollections that are forever melded to our soul. And if their recital becomes a magic moment in our mind's ear in years hence, it won't be the performance, but the private feelings generated by the physical presence of being there. At a drag strip on a glorious day my home-made sports-car captures the trophy, but the thrill was my girl's cheers from the spectator line.

On the rare occasion when Johnny's *Twelfth* plays on our modern audio system in our restored '71 El Camino, it creates pure ear-candy of today's lifetime.

36148465R00124

Made in the USA
San Bernardino, CA
14 July 2016